LAST TRAIN FROM BLACKSTOCK JUNCTION

and other railway stories

by

PAUL SALVESON

Published by Platform 5 Publishing Ltd,
52 Broadfield Road, Sheffield, S8 0XJ, England.

Printed in England by The Amadeus Press, Cleckheaton, West Yorkshire

ISBN 978 1909431 35 5

Preface

These stories were written between 1985 and 2022. That's a long gap, spanning quite a big chunk of my railway career. The earliest was 'A Letter from Mrs Makant' written in 1982 and first published in Locomotive Journal, the ASLE&F magazine. 'Austin's Last Turn' and 'Who Signed the Book?' were written in 1985; the latter was published in Locomotive Journal in December 1985. I've played around with it a bit, though the basic story is the same. 'First Day at the Loco Works' and 'Special Train' formed part of my novel The Works, published in 2020 the week before Lockdown. I've taken the two chapters out and made them into stand-alone stories. Maybe that's cheating, but it seems to work.

The stories, hopefully, reflect life on railways in the North of England during a period of great transition. The focus is on railway people's lives and 'how it was'. So I make no apologies for using language which some people might find offensive – but you'll find far worse in many 'popular' novels.

I must stress that the stories are fictional and none of the characters are 'real' people, living or deceased.

The stories are written to be enjoyed – I hope they will be read by the current generation of railwaymen and women but also by readers from outside the industry. In some cases I have avoided too much technical detail to appeal to a broader audience.

Paul Salveson
Bolton
June 2022

Acknowledgments

Many friends and colleagues have helped with this in various ways – thank you! Any errors, lapses or whatever – it's all down to me....

Safety on the tracks

Some of the stories, particularly 'Last Train from Blackstock Junction', mention events which involve trespass on the tracks. It's not only illegal, it's extremely dangerous. I hope nothing in these stories is interpreted as condoning trespass on the railway. I've known too many friends and colleagues who have been involved in what is referred to as 'an incident', typically the death of a young boy or girl who has thought it 'cool' to wander onto the railway. As well as the unimaginable pain it causes to the families of people who've been killed, the emotional burden on railway staff who have been involved is enormous.

Please, please – don't go on the tracks and tell your kids not to.

Contents

Foreword

The railway is at the heart of the economic, social and political life of our country. No wonder it has such a strong place in the emotional part of our lives, too. Our railways, and particularly the interaction between people, the railway and the landscape, feature powerfully in art and literature.

This series of stories of railway people and the world in which they live, or lived, is a great contribution to railway literature; not only because each is a great story, but because each represents the close observation of those people from a railwayman himself. Working on the railway is a vocation, and has been since the dawn of the steam age. These stories tell you about how things were, and sometimes still are, as well as something of the changes that have affected people's lives as the world of railways has changed.

As you read these, you'll find some history, some romance, some politics, a little prejudice – sadly – and some humour; you will in fact be in the world of railwaymen and women. I hope you find them as absorbing as I did when I read Paul's manuscript. Please enjoy his work!

Sir Peter Hendy CBE
Chair
Network Rail
May 2022

The Station Clock

Preserved LMS 'Jubilee' 5690 "Leander" skirts Morecambe Bay, near Grange-over-Sands, with a special on the Cumbrian Coast Line c 2004.

Grange-over-Sands on a wet evening in January; rain mixed with sleet driving in across Morecambe Bay. Dave Little and his partner Jane Bradshaw had been for a walk along the promenade before collective common sense took over and they retreated back towards the hotel. They walked down High Street, taking shelter in the doorway of an estate agent to escape a particularly torrential downpour.

The couple had decided to take a short break over New Year. Thanks to Covid, it had been a hard year for both. Dave's lecturing job at Leeds University had lost much of its intellectual attraction thanks to Microsoft Teams taking over from human interaction. Jane's life had been tougher, working as a consultant for the NHS in Bradford. Both were coming up for retirement and were ready for it; the stress of the last year was getting to them. A break in the South Lakes would give them time to see Jane's mum, Agnes, in Barrow and do some easy hill walking.

They waited for the rain to pass and idly scanned the properties for sale in the estate agent's window.

"It's more pricey than Leeds," Dave muttered.

"Well, we're not thinking about moving – are we?"

"No, course not. But there could be worse places to live if we ever wanted to."

"You're joking! 'God's waiting room' they call this place – very nice to visit and use as a base for walking but it'd drive us both mad if we had to live here."

"OK, you're right Janey, and very conservative – with a small and large 'C'. We wouldn't fit in. But hey, look at this – 'Old Station Master's House, Kirkhead Crossing – needs renovation but would make a superb home for couple or single-person seeking a quiet life.'"

"Show me. God, it looks a bit of a wreck don't you think? Even an over-grown train-spotter like you should know better."

He took another look. "It's going pretty cheap – £150k or near offer."

The rain had stopped and Jane grabbed Dave's arm, pulling him towards the hotel and the promise of a last glass of wine before bed.

The room had a fine view across the bay towards Morecambe, the Midland Hotel and the nuclear power station. Gazing through the window they could see the Isle of Man ferry coming in to dock at Heysham. A train rumbled past, slowing down to call at Grange, then re-starting and curling round the bay towards Kents Bank, Wraysholme and Cark. The red tail light flickered then disappeared in the distance, leaving only the sound of the train's horn as it approached the crossing before Kents Bank.

"Jane... we were planning to do a walk over to Cartmel tomorrow, why don't we see if we can get an appointment to call in and see that house, just out of curiosity...it's sort of on the way?"

"Bloody hell Dave, you know what curiosity did?"

"Yes, I know, ...but we don't have a cat."

"You're incorrigible...come on, let's get to bed. I'll ring the estate agent first thing but I bet they won't be able to fix anything before we leave on Wednesday."

She rang the estate agents at 9.15, after they'd had breakfast. The woman on the other end of the phone explained that the house was empty and they could only do accompanied viewings. She'd check the diary.

"You're in luck – we've had a cancellation this morning. Could you make 11.30 at the property? Otherwise it would have to be Thursday."

"Thanks – we're heading home on Wednesday but it's OK, if you can do this morning that'd be great. We'll see you there."

They set out just after 11 along the winding, hilly road to Flookburgh. The rain had cleared and the morning sky over the bay was dramatic, changing by the minute with clouds scudding above the sands. They turned off the main road and along a single-track lane dropping down towards the sea. The railway came into view and they could see the house as they approached, past the old tower – an historic landmark now partly in ruins used as farm buildings.

They were a bit early so they parked up by the house and had a look round outside. Jane groaned.

"I see what they mean about requiring renovation! It's a bloody wreck."

Conversation was drowned out by the sound of warning sirens as the barriers opposite the house came down across the road. A minute later a train came into sight and raced over the crossing. The gates lifted, silence returned. A silence not like anything they knew in Leeds.

A car approached down the lane and stopped next to theirs. A well-dressed young woman carrying a file got out, looking the part.

"Hello, I'm Margaret Postlethwaite – or just 'Mags' – nice to meet you. As you can see, the house has seen better days. The last resident – Mr. Benson, the tenant – sadly passed away four years ago and he'd not kept it in very good condition. The owner has been sitting on it since then but finally decided to sell. I know it's a mess, but that's reflected in the asking price. It's got great potential though!"

Margaret struggled with the door key, an old mortice lock that had gone rusty. It finally turned and she opened the door to find a mountain of junk mail piled up behind.

"I think the electricity is still on, let's see if we can get some light..."

The lights came on to reveal two downstairs rooms with an adjoining kitchen. There was a bit of a garden at the side. The front window directly overlooked the line, with distant views of the bay and Humphrey Head beyond.

The stairs led to a couple of small bedrooms and a bathroom, very 1970s style. The windows were UPVC and the downstairs fireplace had been replaced by storage heaters. Whoever had been here, they weren't too interested in preserving heritage features. Not much apart from the shell of the house had survived.

But one thing had – the old clock on the outside of the house, fixed above the front door and sheltered by a decaying timber canopy. It was fixed at 11.45 – the face was in Roman numerals, the traditional railway style.

"The clock's a nice feature isn't it?" the estate agent commented, "doesn't look like it's worked for years though. The station closed way before I was even born, don't think there'd have been much need for a station clock, nobody ever used the train."

Dave and Jane drove back to Leeds on Wednesday; most of the conversation centred on the house. Dave started the discussion as they drove out of Grange towards Lindal.

"We could always buy it as a holiday home, maybe even make a bit of money from renting it out?"

"Well, the red-hot socialist has turned all capitalist now...but there's the small problem of getting the money to buy it in the first place. Capitalists need capital."

"Jane, if we pooled some of our resources we could afford it – just."

"And what about the £30,000 – and maybe more – to make it liveable? Listen, if you really want it, let's sell up and go for it. But after we're both retired; we've not long to go. My mum would be over the moon, she always complains we never see her."

"So that's a 'yes' then?" said Dave, swerving to avoid an oncoming lorry.

"Yes, if we manage to live that long..."

The sale was agreed and their solicitor said she expected completion by June, fitting in well with both their retirement plans. As they signed the contracts, she wryly commented that Dave and Jane would both need to get proper station masters' uniforms to go with the house.

"But won't it be noisy with the trains going so near? Good luck, anyway."

The sale was completed on time. Dave and Jane sold their house in Leeds with no difficulty and decided to stay a few weeks at a nearby pub – The Railway, appropriately enough – while they got stuck in with cleaning and painting, using local tradesmen to do the bigger jobs. They put their furniture into store for the time being.

Jane went at the task with the zeal of a convert, coming up with grandiose ideas for timber-framed doors and windows and Victorian fireplaces in the downstairs rooms.

They got on well with the people who ran the pub, Jack and Brenda Robinson. The family had run the place for years, Jack inheriting it from his dad.

"It's good that someone's tekking the Station House on," said Jack, as he served Dave a pint of his new-found favourite, Loweswater Gold. "It's not had a happy history but don't let that put you off."

"What was that?" overheard Jane. "What happened?"

"Over the years there've been a couple of accidents on the crossing," replied the landlord, warming to his subject. "They sen as there's 'blood on them tracks'. My dad remembers George Huddleston, a platelayer who lived with his family, getting run over right outside the house. Was distracted by something and a train hit him. Left a widow and three kids, though she – I think she was called Edith – carried on as crossing-keeper and kept the house. More recently there was a nasty accident late one night when one of the local lads drove over the crossing without looking. A train went right into the car and killed him outright. It was after that they put those automatic barriers in."

"Huh, the estate agent said nothing about all that," sighed Jane.

"It's not like you to be superstitious," said Dave, putting his arm round her. "Maybe we'll get to know the ghost of the old station master, like 'Ben Isaacs' in that Arthur Askey film, 'The Ghost Train' – or the signalman in the Charles Dickens' story."

"Oh sod off Dave. And don't blame me if it all goes pear-shaped. If there's any ghosts around I'll be away off to mum's in Barrow."

They made good progress on the house; no ghosts were spotted and the incidents recounted by the pub landlord were put aside as they grew more excited about 'moving in' day. They'd filled two skips of rubbish, got local builders to put in a new kitchen, bathroom and – Jane won the argument – traditional timber-framed windows.

Searching the internet, they had dug out some original photos of the Station House, taken around 1900, which they used to get the new fittings as close to the original as possible, which dated back to the line's opening in 1857.

A Furness Railway postcard view of Kents Bank station, c 1920.

"Look at that one, with the family group in front of the house," said Jane. "'Mr and Mrs George Huddleston and family, Kirkhead Station House, 1901.' That was the man Jack told us about in the pub, who was killed on the crossing. Poor chap, and leaving a wife and kids as well."

"...and a crossing-keeper's wage wouldn't have stretched far then, if you'd three kids to bring up on your own. But at least she was able to stay on here."

The local joiner and plumber had turned up on time, did a good job and didn't charge the earth. "Would still be waiting for them to come if we were back in Leeds," said Jane, as she lugged the dining table chairs out of the removal van.

"There's just one thing we should think about," said Dave as they stood outside by the front door, enjoying a break between the unloading. "That clock."

"What do you want to do with it," said Jane. "Can't see it ever being made to work, it's OK where it is."

"Well let's have a look anyway."

He got the ladders out and climbed up to the clock. It was screwed into a wooden panel that was rotten and the whole thing came off easily. Dave triumphantly carried his trophy down the ladder steps.

"Let's take it inside and have a proper look."

They were approaching the front door and a sudden wind slammed the door in Dave's face.

"Where the hell did that come from?" Dave asked himself. Looking round, it was a calm, sunny July day.

"It's that ghost o' George Huddleston, I told yo'," grinned Jane, lapsing into her mum's Barrow accent.

Dave cleared some space on the kitchen table and started unscrewing the back of the clock. The screws were rusty and needed some WD 40 to encourage them, but eventually the back panel pulled off. The mechanism looked as though it was still intact but badly rusted.

"There's no way we're going to get that working," said Dave. "We'd be better off taking it to a clockmaker's, having the old mechanism taken out and putting entirely new battery-operated gear into it. I saw an advert for a place in Grange, shall we see if they can do it?"

"Well, if you want, but let's keep the old mechanism, it'd be a shame to throw it away," said Jane.

The face of the clock was pock-marked with stains from being exposed to decades of harsh weather. But cleaning round it, Dave could make out the words 'Furness Railway' and a serial number.

"Bet this is worth something Jane. If we get stuck we could always sell it on e-bay."

"Oh no we won't," responded Jane. "It's one of the few original bits about the place, apart from the stone and mortar. It stays here – but if you want to get it running, try that place in Grange."

The clockmaker was another Postlethwaite, Harold, who it turns out was Mags' dad.

"Well I never. Furness Railway! It's a fine clock but as you say there's no way that mechanism will ever work. A shame to take it out, but don't be too sentimental. A clock's like a dog – made to work not be an ornament."

As he spoke, Ella, a retriever, came bounding out of the back room. "Though there's always exceptions to the rule, I suppose."

"Right, well if you can go ahead that's great. We want to keep the old mechanism as part of the history of the house but having the clock working again would be the icing on the cake of everything we've done."

"Aye, it'll be a nice touch. Our Margaret told me about you and your wife buying the place. Good to get it occupied after all that trouble."

The clock was ready in just a couple of days. Harold had done a decent job, even to the extent of giving the clock an artificial 'tick-tock' to make it seem a bit more 'real'. Jane wasn't convinced but it appealed to Dave.

Why don't we keep it in the house? asked Jane. "It'd look good in the kitchen and nobody would see it outside above the door. There won't be any passengers turning up for their train to Carnforth or Barrow, checking to see if they were in time."

"OK, let's try it in the kitchen. I'll get a few rawl plugs and screw it into the wall above the dining table."

After weeks of hyper activity – and stress, trying to get everything done, it seemed strange to be able to just relax and do nothing much. A few friends from Leeds came over to see the new place and Jane's mum drove across from Barrow.

"My, it's lovely. And what a great job you've done on it. I love that clock, where did you get it from?" she asked Jane.

"It came with the house – we've had to have the mechanism changed – no way it could've been repaired. But it looks a treat, doesn't it?"

"It does. They say clocks can bring you luck – good and bad, it has to be said. But I hope that's a lucky clock."

Summer progressed into Autumn and the winds coming in across the bay blew stronger. They discovered they had a few neighbours, some of whom they'd met during their three weeks' stay at the pub.

David Braithwaite was a local farmer, one of the few regular users of the crossing. He had two sides two him – the taciturn north Lancashire farmer but with a kinder welcoming side.

"I've brought you a few eggs - and some jam the wife has made. A sort of house-warming present though I know you've been here a few weeks now. Settling in alreet?"

"Oh yes," responded Jane. "And thanks so much for the eggs. I was just going to pop into Flookburgh for some things so I can cross them off the list. Lovely."

"Aye, they'll taste better than those eggs you get in supermarkets from battery hens. Wouldn't touch 'em. Now then, I see the old clock's gone?" he said, looking up to the blank space where the clock had been fixed.

"Well not exactly, Dave took it down and it's in the kitchen. We got a new mechanism put in – it works now."

"Well, I'm glad it does. They sen as that was what, indirectly like, killed George Huddleston."

"How do you mean?"

"Well, this is just hearsay passed down, but my fayther told me as George had had a few bottles of ale an' he decided he'd go out and wind up the clock. Silly bugger, it were well after 11 o' clock at neet and pitch black. Wind blowing like mad. His wife begged him to stay in but he'd have nowt of it. The next thing we know is the sound of a train whistling - and a shout. They found George's body further down the track. A bit of a mess by all accounts. Sorry lass, hope that doesn't upset you. Long time ago, before the Great War. But time moves slow round here."

Dave and Jane had time to explore the area, making the most of the fine country around Cartmel and Grange. A stroll down to Humphrey Head was a regular afternoon outing, by the 'holy well' and up onto the headland where legend says the last wolf in England was killed. Standing on the headland looking out across the bay you could see Morecambe, and round to the west was Ulverston and the Hoad Monument; Barrow further along.

Before the railway was built there was a regular coach service across the bay. It was a perilous journey that had claimed many lives over the centuries. It was discontinued after the railway opened in 1857 though people carried on walking across, using the services of The Guide who lived further round the coast between Kents Bank and Grange.

It was a typically wet and windy night in late October. The last train of the day was the Manchester Airport to Barrow, reporting number 1C50. It was powered by one of the new class 195 trains – 'Pride of Cumbria.' The last train from 'the south' to Barrow has been known by generations of railway folk and locals as 'The Whip' – though nobody knows why.

The driver was Jimmy Helm, an old-hand Barrow man who had started on the railway as an engine cleaner at Carnforth, not long after the end of steam. He'd been booked as a driver at Barrow for 25 years and was coming up to retirement.

Jack had company from Preston – his old mate Derek Graham who was booked to return to Barrow 'as passenger' after bringing in a train from Windermere. He was sitting in the front coach behind Jimmy, and joined him – against the rules but no prying eyes would be around at that time of night – after they left Carnforth. The train gradually emptied, handfuls of people getting out at Silverdale, Arnside and Grange.

At Kents Bank a couple of regulars got on, heading home to Barrow after seeing friends. They waved to Jack from the platform as they joined the train, thankful to get into the warmth. After the doors had closed he got the 'right away' signal from Jenny, the guard.

It had started to rain – hard. That sort of icy, horizontal rain that comes in off Morecambe Bay when it has a mind to, which is frequently.

"Well Derek, just a few months to go and that's it. I'll be able to get me feet up or do a spot o' fishin."

"Aye, an' I won't be far behind you! I've had enough o' 4 a.m. starts and late finishes like this."

The train gathered speed and swept round the curve past Humphrey Head and Wyke Farm, rain lashing across the train's windscreen making visibility difficult. They'd left Kents Bank on time at 23.43 and were hoping for a slightly early finish at Barrow.

It wasn't to be.

Jack had expected the signal controlling Kirkhead Crossing to be showing 'green' – and it was, together with a flashing white signal to tell the driver that the crossing was working correctly.

A couple of seconds later Jack looked through the rain-spattered windscreen in horror. The gates were open to the road and there was what looked like a horse and cart, or carriage, galloping towards the crossing.

"Bloody'ell! What in fuck's name....." shouted Jack as he threw the train brake into a full emergency application. The train rocked violently.

Derek had instinctively crouched down behind the control panel to avoid any shattered glass hitting him. Jack just looked on in shock. The next moment there was a loud bang and a flash, with the snorts of a distressed horse. In the train there were screams of panic as the train shuddered to a violent halt.

The train's brakes had taken effect quickly and the three-coaches came to a stand about a hundred yards beyond the crossing.

"You alreet mate?" Derek asked.

"Well I'm not hurt. But fuckin' hell, what was that?"

"Buggered if I know but we'll go and see. Better get the 'red button' pressed so the signaller and Control know we've a problem. We could be here a while."

The conductor, Jenny Johnson, had been issuing tickets to the couple who'd got on at Kents Bank when she was thrown to the floor as the train lurched to a stop. She was just behind the cab door.

"You guys OK? What happened?"

"I wish we knew – we had a green – didn't we Derek? – yet the gates were open and some sort of horse-drawn carriage ran across. We hit it, I'm sure. That's as much as I can say. Let's have a look at the train and see if there's any damage. Jenny, tell the passengers what's happening and put some clips down on the `up' line to mek sure we're protected."

Jenny put on her 'hi-vis' jacket and jumped onto the track with the regulation pair of track circuit operating clips, which fixed across the rails put signals to danger, if they weren't already. Just to make sure they were on, she gave each clip a good stamping with her boots.

The Ulverston 'bobby' had been alerted by the emergency signal – the 'red button' – and the cab telephone rang within a few seconds.

Arthur Pickstone, the signaller, had been looking forward to a quiet night.

"Hello Signaller. This is an emergency call. This is the driver of 1C50 stopped in advance of Signal U24. I think we've just struck summat at Kirkhead Crossing. Can you confirm signaller that all lines are blocked so I can go down and safely inspect. Thank you."

"By the hell, I wondered where you'd got to," Pickstone replied. "Is everyone OK? Control is aware of the situation and all I can tell you is wait for further instructions. There's nothing on the 'up' now until the 5 a.m. Airport but take care all the same. I can confirm that both lines are blocked. It's bloody strange, everything was working OK at this end, the gates were shown as down and you had a green signal."

"You're telling me it's strange – I had a green and the flashing whites but the barriers seemed to be up – and this horse and cart, or something, went across and it sounded as though we'd hit it. Anyway, stay awake and I'll let you know if we find owt. I've got a driver travelling home passenger with us and he'll assist, as well as my guard."

Jack climbed down onto the track with his lamp to see if there was any damage, or sign of what he might have hit. He was prepared for the worst, having been involved in another crossing accident years ago near Millom. Some poor old demented sod had wandered onto the line and the train hit him full on. There wasn't much of him left. It made an awful mess of the train too.

This time there was no scene of squashed bodies with blood, skin and bone smattered around the front. Nothing at all, as far as he could see. Derek had gone back with Jenny, reassuring the few passengers on the train that everything was OK but they could be stuck a while. Most of them took it well, though one character who'd been on the ale at Lancaster started shouting the odds about compensation.

"Everyone will get compensation, don't worry about that – I'll go round with forms for you to fill in and claim, we're just checking there are no casualties," said Jenny. "Arsehole", she thought to herself.

Derek looked round towards the crossing and sure enough the gates were down – the train had stopped within the overlap that prevented the gates going back up for road traffic – not that there'd be any traffic at that time of night.

The Control duty manager at Manchester, Dave Parkinson, rang Jimmy a few minutes later after Jimmy's initial check round the train – which had revealed nothing. Dave had started his railway career at Carnforth so knew the line well.

"Hello driver – that's Jimmy Helm isn't it? I knew you when I was Signalling Manager at Barrow back in the '90s. You OK? What's happened?"

Jimmy explained, as best he could, what he'd seen and how he had reacted, adding that he'd done as good an inspection of the train as he could – it was a dark night and the rain was still coming down in buckets – and nothing had been found.

"Bloody hell Jimmy, that's some story. Listen, I'm going to send out some relief for you – you've had a nasty shock. Cliff Rudge was just signing off and he owed me a favour, so he's on his way in a taxi – just hope the driver can find you. Des Melia, the on-call DTM is with him and Network Rail has been informed; their Mobile Ops Manager is on his way from Lancaster so you'll have quite a party! How's your conductor? Is she OK? I'll try and raise her on-call Conductor Team Manager if need be?"

Jenny responded saying she was fine apart from a bit of a bruised knee after the sudden stop and dragging the on-call CTM out on a night like this would be over-kill.

"Good, it was starting to get a bit over-crowded. We've sent out for technicians from Newton Heath to have a closer look under the train – as close as possible on a dark night anyway – and that's going to take some time. The taxi will take the five passengers; you and your mate go back to Barrow on the train with your conductor, which will run as empty to depot."

Derek managed to walk down the four-foot, in the driving rain, towards the Station House. It was in darkness. Dave and Jane's car was parked outside suggesting they were at home in bed. He thought it wise to let the occupants know what had happened – and there might be a brew going, though they might not appreciate being woken up at half past midnight.

He rang the doorbell and after a couple of minutes some lights came on and Dave opened the door.

"I'm really sorry to disturb you sir. I'm the driver of the Barrow train and there's been an incident here at the crossing. We can't see anything amiss but we've had to make an emergency stop. The train is just down the line." Derek pointed to the red tail light of the beleaguered express.

"Did you hear anything, about fifteen minutes ago? We seemed to hit something, looked like a horse and carriage of some kind, and it made a huge bang."

Dave looked nonplussed. "I'm quite a light sleeper but I didn't hear anything. Look, would you like to come in and have a cup of tea? You look in a bit of a state. If there are others bring them down and we'll get the kettle on."

"That's very kind but the rules say we've got to keep the passengers on the train for the time being – if we have hit something we don't want to give them any nasty shocks. But we will need to get the passengers out of the train eventually, when the taxi arrives to take them home; we could be stuck for hours. It's not a nice night to be standing around in the middle of nowhere – if you don't mind me saying so – with no shelter."

"Sure, fully understand. Tell you what – we'll get the kettle on and make a pot of tea and you can take it back to the train, cups and milk provided as well!"

The five passengers, as well as Jimmy, Derek and Jenny, appreciated the tea and biscuits; even the drunk. He'd sobered up a bit by now.

"We'll keep an eye out for the taxi," said Jane, before Derek walked back to the train. "A lot of taxis don't know the area, just hope he's not got lost and ended up in Grange. What time is it Dave?"

Another half hour passed; Dave and Jane stayed up to greet the taxi. "Oh shit, the clock has stopped. It's still showing 11.45. Hang on, I'll get the phone out. It's 1 o'clock now and I think I can hear something coming down the lane – must be the taxi."

The cab stopped just short of the crossing, with a Network Rail 4x4 just behind with Cathy Huddleston, the on-call Ops Manager driving; Cliff Rudge and Des Melia got out, offering to help the train crew get the passengers safely down the track to the crossing.

Knowing the 'up' line was blocked the small group of passengers and railway staff was led down the track by Jenny, using her lamp to show the way.

She saw the passengers into the taxi and told the driver to drop two off at Ulverston then head direct for Barrow with the rest. Checks had been made at Cark and Dalton just in case anyone was waiting and luckily no-one was – or they'd given up and ordered a cab.

Jimmy got onto the signalman at Ulverston and told him the taxi was on its way to Barrow. "Thanks driver. Control has said the rolling stock technicians should be with you soon."

Clive Draper and Ash Patel were there by 2.15 a.m., greeting Clive with characteristic Manchester humour.

"Hello driver, what have you got for us then? Hope it's not too grisly because we've only just had our supper."

A more thorough inspection produced the same result as Jimmy's. There was nothing apparent. "What they'll probably do," said Ash, "is send the train to Newton Heath for a more detailed inspection tomorrow. If this train has hit anything – and we can't see owt – they'll soon know."

Cliff Rudge, now the driver of the train, rang Ulverston box to say that the train was ready to proceed following the inspection. Jenny had checked the gates as best she could in the darkness and they seemed to be working OK.

"Thanks driver, you're right away to depot then. And I can catch up on my night's reading – it's a ghost story! But mebbe yours is better!"

Derek and Jenny thanked the couple. "We're really grateful for all your help; some folk would have slammed the door in our faces and told us to get lost!"

"I'm really glad we could help and hope you get to the bottom of the mystery. Let us know if you hear anything," said Jane as Derek turned towards his train, feeling even more baffled as to what he and Jimmy had experienced.

Cliff took the controls and the train moved forward – Jimmy and Derek sat at the table behind the cab door.

"So you're telling me that you saw a horse and carriage galloping over the crossing and you think you hit it – but there's no trace of any damage? Had you two been on the piss in Preston?" shouted

Cliff from the cab. "You couldn't make it up though, I'll give you that. And to be honest, and seriously, I know you two aren't ale cans."

Jimmy, Derek and Jenny signed off at 3.45 a.m. after each had completed an incident report. They knew they hadn't heard the last of it. The duty supervisor told them Control had said they were to phone in at 12.00 noon and they'd take it from there, but they were not expected to take up their booked work. "For your own good – you've had a fright, especially you Jimmy," Eddie Wilson, the supervisor added.

They were asked to appear the following afternoon before their Driver Manager at Barrow. It was Mary Harrop, an experienced manager with ten years' driving behind her, but half the age of both the drivers.

She was polite and deferential to Jimmy and Derek, seeing each individually, offering them cups of tea. They told the same story of what they'd seen happen. Derek was the second interviewee.

"Derek, you and Jimmy have had unblemished careers and I know you're both coming up for retirement. All we can see is that you made an emergency stop at Kirkhead Crossing. That's OK, you didn't go through a red, nothing untoward happened. If I was you, off the record, I'd keep quiet about this 'horse and carriage' story. I'm not saying I don't believe you. I don't know what to believe. But if it went to Rail Accident Investigation Branch I can't see them swallowing it. Can you?"

"No, Mary, you're right. But it's a queer do that we both saw this bloody nag, and heard one hell of a bang. And both of us saw the barriers were up. What d'you mek o'that?"

"We've had a preliminary report from Network Rail on the barriers at Kirkhead and they say they're working normally and no fault has been detected. Same with the signal that protects the crossing. So we're still none the wiser. The 195 has been sent to Newton Heath for examination, let's see if they can find any trace of it hitting something. For now, I'm giving both you and your mate a week's sick leave. Whatever did happen that night it might have an effect on you and your alertness so we're not taking any chances. In fact, let's make it two weeks. OK?"

It was coming up to Christmas so a couple of weeks paid leave wasn't unwelcome to either of them. Jenny was given two days off.

"I'd give you a bit longer chuck but we're short-handed and we're already having to cancel trains because we've no guards," the CTM, Janice Pickering, explained.

Jimmy's wife, Alex, had been saying she fancied a trip to Grange to visit Higginson's the local butchers, so how about a run out in the car next week, she suggested.

That gave Jimmy an idea. It would be good to call in at the Station House and personally thank the people there and have a look at the place in daylight.

The car meandered down the lane from Allithwaite and pulled up outside the Station House. Dave was doing a bit of work outside, making the most of the mild November weather.

"Hello, I don't know if you remember me but I was one of the drivers on the train that made the emergency stop last week. Just called round to thank you for your hospitality. It was really appreciated."

"No problem at all, we don't get much excitement round here and it has certainly given us something to talk about. And we've been doing a bit of our own research. Come in and have a cup of tea."

Jimmy and Alex went into the sitting room where they'd been on 'that night', feeling much less stressed than Jimmy had been then. Jane joined the company.

"I'm glad you called round," Jane said as she placed the coffee and cakes on the table. "After last week we've been doing a bit of digging on the area and found some things that might interest you.

An ancient milestone at Cartmel.

Back in the 1850s, when the railway was being constructed, there was still a horse carriage service, a few days a week, from Ulverston to Lancaster, 'over the sands'. It didn't last long after the railway opened – it was unreliable and dangerous. What probably killed it off was a terrible accident that happened in November 1857 when it tried to cross the bay on a stormy night." Jane poured out the coffee before continuing.

"The Westmorland Gazette had a lot to say about it – the carriage, carrying four people, plus a driver and guide, got lost in the sands and it was only a couple of days later when the bodies started to appear, washed up at Kents Bank and Humphrey Head. The coach driver was never found, probably got washed out into the sea. The route the coach took was this crossing by our house, then round by Kirkhead Hall to Kents Bank – and then headed across the sands. It was a stormy night, the driver took a big risk, and he paid for it. The coach left Ulverston at 11.00 pm so would have been at the crossing by around 11.45 – the time when you saw what you thought was a horse-drawn carriage."

"Well, thanks, that's really very interesting. I've seen paintings of the carriages crossing the sands, led by teams of horses. I thought that had finished by the early 1800s." Jimmy gazed into his coffee.

"Have another biscuit James – they are very nice – then we'd better get on our way," announced Mrs Helm, lowering the tension.

"Thanks once again for your kindness," said Jimmy. "If I hear anything from the examination of the train I'll let you know."

Two days later Jimmy's mobile rang. "Hello Jimmy, it's Mary here at Preston. We've had some results back from Newton Heath. The examination of the Class 195 unit didn't produce much more than the usual bits and bobs that trains pick up – remains of birds that had got in the way, a few branches, general muck. But they did find traces of timber – polished wood to be precise – at the front end. One of our 'Year in Industry' students said she could take a sample of the wood to the university and ask one of her mates in the labs if they could do an analysis of it. Now this is where it does get interesting. The bit of wood was well over a hundred years old. Probably 150 years or even more. There was some lacquer on one side, the sort used by coach makers back in the 1840s on both traditional horse-drawn carriages and early railway carriages. This sample also showed some trace of, well, to put it crudely, horse shit. So you don't need to be Sherlock Holmes to think it was the remains of a horse-drawn carriage from the 1850s which our 21st century train had managed to hit. Or might have done. Maybe. What do you think of that then?"

There was a long silence on the phone at Jimmy's end. "So d'you think my story – and Derek's – about hitting a horse and carriage isn't such a fantasy after all?"

"I'm not saying I've changed my mind – and I don't see how we could take this to RAIB and expect them to believe us. And it wasn't a reportable accident anyway. But I thought it might give you and Derek some peace of mind. As far as the company's concerned, case closed. Enjoy your leave and please don't see any more ghosts, OK? And by the way, you know the company takes a dim view of unauthorised members of staff riding with the driver?"

The following day – Jimmy was still on his enforced leave – he decided to call round again at the Station House and tell the couple what he'd been told. Dave was out – Jane said he'd been at the clockmaker's getting the old clock mended after it had stopped the other night. Dave came through the door, holding the ancient time-piece.

"Postlethwaite said there didn't seem anything wrong with it – put a new battery in but it was working alright before. Just a quirk."

Dave and Jane settled into life at Kirkhead. Christmas came and went and they were able to get out and do more exploring around the South Lakes. Retirement was doing both of them good – no more of the occasional rows, no stressful 'Teams' meetings. And the clock was keeping perfect time. Spring came around, one of those magnificent seasons where the valleys of the Winster, Duddon and Rusland Pool were full of colour and warmth.

It was a Saturday, May 7th. Dave and Jane had been out for a long walk over Hampsfell, getting home in time for a late supper followed by an early night.

It was Dave who first heard something, at about quarter to twelve.

It seemed to be coming from Ulverston way. Nothing could have prepared him for what he saw. The sky was completely ablaze and opening the window he heard a seemingly endless succession of explosions and what sounded like heavy gunfire.

"Jane, come here...I can't believe this is happening."

"Where's it coming from? It must be Barrow – it's well beyond Ulverston. It looks like the whole town's on fire......What's going on? There was nothing on the news. Are we at war? Or at the receiving end of some sort of terrorist attack? If one of those nuclear subs goes up the whole of Cumbria could go with it."

Dave stood at the window, staring in shock. The explosions continued, with the sound of counter-attack fire coming from below. What looked like an aircraft burst into flames, downed by the ground fire.

The next moment they heard loud banging on the front door.

"Help! Please let us in! Help!"

Dave dashed down the stairs and opened the door – to find nothing. The rain was lashing against the porch and he checked up and down the lane – there was no sign of anything.

He went back upstairs. The sound of explosions in the distance continued and through the rain they could see the flames getting higher. After two minutes the banging started again. "Please help us! Let us in!"

This time they both went down, with a torch and some trepidation. The door blew open with the wind, Jane was drenched by a squall of rain. There was no-one to be seen.

"Look, let's make ourselves a brew – we're not going to get any sleep with all this going on – and if we do get any more visits at least we'll be downstairs. Maybe it's kids playing stupid games."

"Dave, come off it. What kids? And at half past midnight? Any naughty boys will be safely packed up in bed. We're not in Headingley now!"

It was then that Jane made a sudden realisation. "Mum! Oh my God Dave, she could be in the middle of all that. I've got to ring her."

She rushed downstairs picking up the landline which was placed on the kitchen table below the clock. The phone rang for what seemed an eternity until at last she heard a voice.

"Who's that ringing at this time?"

"Mum, it's me, Jane. Are you alright?"

"Course I'm bloody well alright, at least I was before you woke me up. What's the matter?"

"Oh, well.... nothing really, we just keep hearing explosions that seem to be coming from Barrow way. You sure you're OK?"

"Yes love, I am. Have you been on the wine again? We're alright here, get some sleep," as she put the phone down.

Jane stood still for some time. She noticed that the clock had stopped again, at its usual time of 11.45. Bloody clockmaker! It would have to go back in the morning. Hopefully he wouldn't charge.

She went back upstairs; the fires had disappeared and the explosions had stopped. All that remained was a gentle whistling through the trees and the sound of the barriers coming down as a slightly-delayed Barrow train – the 'Whip' – came rattling over the crossing.

Jane and Dave settled back down to bed; neither could sleep. She mentioned the clock stopping again.

"I'm sure that clock has something to do with all this. All the bad things here have happened at 11.45. It can't be a coincidence. Come on Jane, we've both got PhDs, we should be able to get to the bottom of this."

That morning, before taking the clock back to Grange, Jane got on the internet and googled 'Barrow – bombings'. Wikipedia described the events of May 1941:

"The difficulty of solely targeting Barrow's shipyard meant that many residential neighbourhoods were bombed instead; 83 civilians were killed, 330 injured, and over 10,000 houses were damaged or destroyed during the Blitz, about 25 percent of the town's housing stock. Surrounding towns and villages were often mistaken for Barrow and were attacked instead, while many streets in Barrow were severely damaged. Bombing during mid-April 1941 caused significant damage to a central portion of Abbey Road, completely destroying the Waverley Hotel as well as Christ Church and the Abbey Road Baptist Church. The town's main public baths and Essoldo Theatre were also severely damaged, however they were repaired within years. Hawcoat Lane is a street that is most noted for taking a direct destructive hit in early May 1941. Barrow has been described as somewhat unprepared for the Blitz, as there were only enough public shelters for 5 percent of the town's population; some people who lived in the town centre were even forced to seek refuge in hedgerows on the outskirts of Barrow. This shortage of shelters was believed to have led to excessively high casualties."

The worst of the bombings took place on May 7th, with the bombardment starting the previous night, just before midnight. Other reports told of terrified Barrovians fleeing the blitz, getting trains or buses – if they could – to surrounding towns and villages where they hoped they'd be safe. A train left Barrow that evening bound for Carnforth, packed with people escaping to wherever they could – Dalton, Ulverston, Cark – and Kirkhead. It departed minutes before the station suffered a direct hit. Many families were said to have taken shelter in strangers' homes, barns or just on roadsides. Anything would be better than the bombing.

"Look at this Dave. This is what we saw last night. Or imagined what we saw. 80 years to the day. I remember mum talking about it all, stories her mum had told her. She lived at the bottom of Abbey Road which copped some of the worst of it. She was lucky, but some of the houses nearby were destroyed and several of her neighbours died. She helped pull some of the bodies out of the rubble, including little kids. Grandad was away in North Africa, with the Lancashire Fusiliers. When he came back and saw the town he said it looked like they'd had it worse than anything Rommel threw at them. And that hammering on the door – was it something to do with those poor people fleeing the bombing – eighty years ago?"

The series of events was starting to take its toll. Rows between Dave and Jane became more common, almost as bad as when they were both doing stressful jobs. Jane was starting to think they should put the house up for sale. They'd get their money back, even with all the extra work they'd done.

Dave took the clock back to Postlethwaite's. He had some sympathy for what Jane was saying.

"Good morning David," Harold looked up from his current 'patient' as he called them and put down his pipe. "Not more problems with that railway clock? Let's have a look."

The battery was tested and was OK; the clock had started working that morning, after Dave had re-set the fingers.

"Do you think there's something odd about the clock?" Dave asked. "I mean...something supernatural. Sounds weird I know. We've been doing some research and it seems that all the bad things – fatal accidents, imagined fires and explosions – seem to happen around the same time of night, 11.45, and the clock stops working. I'd have said it was just coincidence if it was a couple of times, but it's more than that."

Postlethwaite sat down on his bench and re-lit his pipe, aping his hero, Harold Wilson.

"Strange things happen Dave. Have you ever heard of the Timberbottom Skulls, over Bolton way? Nobody knows who these skulls were, but they were peaceful enough and didn't trouble a soul. They'd been displayed in a farmhouse for many, many years, with a legend that they should never be moved. Then some bright spark came along and moved 'em. They didn't like it. They created havoc. It was only when they were put back in their original resting place that the trouble stopped. It may sound a mad idea, but why not put the clock back in its original place; I'll fit the old mechanism – happy to do it, as favour, and I'll sort you out with a nice retro-style Victorian clock for the kitchen."

Dave returned the following day with the clock and the old mechanism which they'd been lucky enough to keep in a bottom drawer, following Jane's intervention. Postlethwaite took out the new battery-powered mechanism there and then, and put back the old clockwork machinery.

"Pity it'll never work. But good luck – let's hope these strange goings-on come to an end. I'll order one of those repro railway clocks for you. They cost about £60 and look OK."

Jane had already been up the ladders and fixed a new wooden batten on the wall above the front door. She was a better DIY-er than Dave, though he wouldn't admit it.

"Well done love! Let's give it a coat or two of paint to protect it from the weather and we'll mount the clock tomorrow."

It was another fine day and after breakfast Dave volunteered to fix the clock back into place. Three long screws went easily into the batten, fixing the clock firmly in place. Dave went back down the ladders, pleased with his efforts.

Neither of them noticed that the clock had started to work.

Tick-tock-tick-tock – tick-tock

Many thanks to all who have helped with technical advice, particularly Chris, Jason and Tim.
Note that this is a work of fiction, loosely based on a particular part of the Furness Peninsula. The characters are entirely fictional. Barrow was badly hit during the Second World War and the story is told in detail through displays in the town's Dock Museum. Barrow station did suffer a direct hit but the part of the story about a train taking people out of the town is imagined – but may well have happened. See 'The Barrow Blitz', by Bryn Trescatheric.

Austin's Last Turn

Signalman Frank Dickinson at work in Bolton East Junction signal box, a few weeks before it closed.

Austin had a formative influence on my career as a railwayman. Coming up to 75 I wanted to write down something about him and the other 'characters' whom I had the privilege to work with back then, when it was a very different railway. They've all long since signed off – and mostly died. We shall not see their like again – particularly the likes of Austin Shorrock.

His railway career ended abruptly, at the age of 55. It was 1985. Most of his workmates were surprised at his decision to finish, but they really didn't know Austin. Few people did.

What I was able to piece together about his life is far from complete. He never married and left no children who could offer stories about his life outside the railway. He always lived in the 'family' home in Great Lever, just outside Bolton, in a terraced house facing the railway. By the time I knew him, in my early thirties, it was just him and his mother living there. He was devoted to her, despite the dementia she was starting to show.

He had a younger brother, Arnold, who had spent his working life in the cotton industry. The two were not particularly close but over a cup of tea in Lyons' Coffee House Arnold offered me a few hints about Austin's life and showed me a couple of early photos of the family, on holiday in Blackpool. Nothing much new came out of the conversation. I already knew that he was 'musical' and loved his Beethoven, Mozart and Haydn. I remember him using up one of his passes to travel to a book dealer in York to collect a rare copy of 'The Symphonies of Joseph Haydn'. I met him getting off the train at Trinity Street, looking very pleased with his prize. He used to give an occasional lecture for the local WEA on music appreciation.

Austin Shorrock was an anachronism by 1985. He fitted uneasily with the 20th century, seeming to personify the image of a late Victorian craftsman with his stiff, and mostly unsmiling, self-respect. A gold watch hung from his railway-issue waistcoat, bearing the onion-shaped time-piece that had belonged to his grandfather. You would never see him without a tie.

Railways ran in the family and it was the vocation of 'signalman' that had called three generations of Shorrocks. Alfred Shorrock started as a 'box lad' at Bolton No. 2 box in 1916; he was forced to retire through ill-health at the age of 75 from his 'Special Class Relief' job. His son George spent thirty years in the signalling grades before taking up a position as signalling inspector in the Bury area. He retired from 'the service' at the relatively young age of 71, enjoying his railway pension for six months before collapsing with a heart attack.

Austin's railway career also began as a box lad – at Bolton No. 1, in 1945 at the age of 14. He worked with his dad, George. Austin was disappointed that he hadn't had chance to 'do his bit' in the war, but took easily to life in the signalbox.

His official role was to record all the train movements, as well as any other incidents, in the Train Register Book. This was kept on a tall desk, the equivalent of a church altar, worn down by generations of signalmen and box-lads until the desk lid formed a crescent shape. He worked to the signalman's instructions, the high priest of this holy of holies to which entry was a privilege, not a right.

Austin learned the job quickly. By the end of his first week he'd mastered all the different bell codes and knew every train that passed the box on the early shift. Most trains were '3-1' on the block bell, for an ordinary passenger train. The morning Glasgow express had the more elevated '4' while a humble goods train, loose-coupled, was a '1-4'. The bell codes were a well-established means of communication which allowed the signalman to act fast in an emergency. If he got a '6' from an adjoining box it meant 'obstruction danger' and all signals would be put back to danger. The signalmen had 'unofficial' bell codes such as '1-2-1' for the approach of an inspector – a 'black mac' – typically a poacher turned gamekeeper.

Signalmen were expected to call the neighbouring box's attention by a single beat of the bell, which the signalman would respond with his own single beat, followed by the actual request 'is line clear for 'xxxxx train''. If the line was clear, the signalman could then 'accept' the train on his block instrument to show 'line clear' and pull off his signals – home board, then starter and lastly the distant showing all signals were clear.

In many places the job was too busy to use the 'call attention' signal so you'd get a cacophony of bell signals sometimes coming at you from three or four directions. Not 'putting on the one's' was against the rules and was only used when there was nobody of authority about, when it would be a case of 'working straight up'.

Austin loved the sound of the bells, with each adjoining box having its own distinctive tone – Green Lane, Bolton No. 2, Darcy Lever.

Though his father was a strict task master and not given to the sort of horse-play that many of his colleagues engaged in (some boxes were noted for the occasional cricket matches down the length of the cabin, during slack periods), he allowed his son to take turns on the 'block bells', tapping out the '3-1' "is line clear for ordinary passenger train?" or whatever might be coming down the line.

The signals and points were controlled by heavy metal levers, with the handles kept brightly polished – each signalman using his preferred metal polish, a job usually delegated to the box lad. A cloth was used to pull the levers, to avoid spoiling the burnished levers. After a couple of weeks Austin was permitted to 'pull off' particular levers – a job requiring strength but above all technique.

There was never any doubt that Austin would make an excellent signalman; his father as much as said that, not that he was given to excessive praise. "Aye, th' lad'll be awreet", he said to his mates in the Railway Club.

Signalling was in the blood; more than a job – a calling. The family DNA would have shown it, with red, yellow and green signals. I remember stories, which I'm sure were true, of son, father and grand-father sitting in 'the front room' of the family home in Great Lever quizzing each other on the Rule Book, Regulations for Train Signalling and Signalmen's General Instructions. They made their own entertainment in those days, for sure.

At the age of 18 Austin was sent to Signalling School at Hunt's Bank, Manchester. The place had an ancient model railway which allowed trainees to see how trains were signalled in every conceivable situation. The instructor, Harry Hindle, told his mate that Austin could come in and run the school himself, his knowledge being remarkable 'for a young lad'. Needless to say he passed with flying colours and applied for a vacancy at Tonge Viaduct, a small box about a mile out of Bolton. He took charge just after his 18th birthday in November 1948.

It wasn't a busy box. An hourly 'passenger' each way with the odd heavy freight to Carlisle, and some goods traffic on the branch to Halliwell Sidings. It was situated high above Folds Road, on Tonge Viaduct – at the 'V' of the two lines diverging to Blackburn or into the goods yard. The wind would blow up from underneath the box making it a cold and draughty place to work. But you had a good view of the surrounding mills and factories.

After a year he put in for a vacancy at a larger box, Croal Bridge Junction, which was a 'Class B' – one step up from the less well-paid 'A' that was Tonge Viaduct. Not that Austin was that bothered about the money; there was more traffic, including coal trains coming down from Linnyshaw Moss, making it an interesting place to work. From the rear of the box you had a view of the River Croal and the Rossendale hills rising up in the distance; though on 'days' you didn't have much time to enjoy the panorama.

He got to know some of the drivers and firemen from Bolton shed who would call in for a brew before working trains to local power stations. Unlike some of the signalmen he was hospitable, as long as the men took off their boots on entry to the box. He didn't want his lino floor getting messed up by oily footwear. Once the formalities had been completed they would be treated to brews of tea and a chat about the state of the railways.

Those years after the war weren't easy. 1948 was one of the coldest winters on record, and though he kept the box warm, with the stove blazing, the outside toilet frequently froze. There were staff shortages and plenty of overtime working – 12 hours, Sundays, rest days. The job, partly out of necessity, became his life. And he was content.

He used his passes to travel around Britain, usually to visit places of railway interest, such as the Forth Bridge and Ribblehead Viaduct. His reading was confined to a few novels and the more serious works of railway history as well as musical biographies.

He was proud to be a 'union man' and attended the branch meetings when shifts allowed. He was elected signalmen's rep on the Local Departmental Committee (LDC) when Ernie Pollitt retired in 1962. He was never a revolutionary, but would stand up – firmly but quietly – for the men's rights. He was often asked to attend conferences, go on to the district council and perform other union activities. But no, he was fine where he was and saw no reason to 'become an activist'. Suggestions from Jack Charlesworth, the District Signalling Inspector, that he apply for a supervisor's job got equally short, but polite, shrift.

The 1960s and 1970s were years of decline and retrenchment for the railways, particularly in the North. The Beeching cuts of the mid to late 1960s saw many of the lines around Bolton disappear, including the once-busy Rochdale route. Goods yards closed and the once mighty Lancashire and Yorkshire Railway warehouse on Manchester Road echoed to nothing but silence. It was pulled down in the 1980s, five years after it handled its last wagon, to make way for a retail park.

Croal Bridge Junction handled less and less traffic. Inside the box there was a growing number of 'white levers' – those that no longer controlled points and signals and were not in use. The pits which had produced the coal that came down the branch shut in the early 1970s. 'Croal Bridge Junction' became a misnomer; it was reduced to being just a 'block post' controlling trains shuttling between Bolton and Manchester, with dreary diesel units instead of steam.

The railway he'd known since boyhood began to change in other ways. The bosses he'd had in the '50s and early '60s had made their way up from the 'wages grades' and knew the job back to front.

You'd struggle to 'get one over' them; the new breed were different. Austin resented the young 'whizz-kids' straight out of university who were taken on as management trainees, most of them knowing little about the job.

One of them turned up at Croal Bridge when Austin was on afternoons, calmly walking into the box to do a routine inspection 'without so much as a by your leave'. Austin told him to go back out and knock.

His father died in 1973, leaving Austin to look after his mum who was increasingly house-bound. Ironically, his father's death created a vacancy at Green Lane, close to home and a higher grade than Croal Bridge, Class D. His mates, out of Austin's ear-shot, talked of 'dead dad's shoes'.

His new box had none of the external attractions of Croal Bridge, being sandwiched between the towering Beehive Mills, a wagon repair works and the malodorous Walker's Tannery.

A quiet day at Newton Heath signal box. Note the large number of white 'out of use' levers.

But he was happy at Green Lane, though it wasn't as busy as it had been in the 1960s. It used to control access to the loco sheds which had closed in 1968 with the end of steam. But it was still busy enough, with traffic going in and out of the parcels depot and ballast sidings. He liked the 'feel' of the box with its coal-fired stove, polished brass 'block bells' and the classic Lancashire and Yorkshire Railway block instruments.

The cosy but ragged armchair was an unofficial addition to the furniture. Every box had one and it allowed signalmen to get their feet up when it was quiet – usually on nights. The company's attempt to remove them 'as a fire hazard' resulted in a rare display of signalmen's militancy, with an all-out strike threatened. The chairs stayed.

One of Austin's other passions, apart from music, was pigeons. Not racing pigeons or homing pigeons, just any sort of pigeon, usually feral ones. This occasionally got him into trouble. A regular routine when he was on 'lates' was to get the bus into town and buy a sack of feed to take back to the house, hiring a taxi to get back. Austin never owned a car and either cycled or walked to work. The taxi was his one 'extravagance'. And only one driver would do, Ibrahim Patel whom Austin befriended, after a fashion. I met him just the once when the bird feed delivery was being made and heard the driver addressing 'Mister Austin' in the most respectful of terms.

Each day Austin would emerge from his house with a bucket of feed and lay it on the track close to the signalbox. Word had got round the pigeon community that a feast was to be had in Bolton and it wasn't uncommon to see a black cloud of pigeonry descending onto the tracks. Complaints were made by some of the drivers whose sighting of signals was blocked by the descending flock of birds. On one occasion it led to a verbal warning from the Area Manager, but Austin ignored it.

I was on lates one day – in June 1982 I think – I received a call from Austin on the circuit phone. He asked if I could take some photographs of him and his mother for his railway I.D. card, knowing I did a bit of photography. It was a rare opportunity to enter Austin's home, though it had little to distinguish it from any other Bolton terraced house, apart from the picture of Beethoven over the fireplace.

I was offered tea and biscuits by 'mum' and then took the photos of Austin out in the back yard. The real reason for my visit was then revealed. Austin had 'adopted' a lame pigeon which he was nursing back to health and wanted me to get a photograph of 'Jimmy'. The pigeon was brought out from the shed and Austin lovingly held it in his hand. I willingly obliged and popped round the following week with the prints.

He had a clever way of dealing with management which combined a degree of politeness with cunning. On one occasion I found myself in a bit of trouble following a box inspection by some kid straight out of college who had been promoted to 'Assistant Area Manager'. He looked round the box – refusing the offer of a cup of tea, which I found impolite – and gazed at a list of telephone numbers I had pinned up above the desk. Two days later I received a 'please explain' noting that a list of telephone numbers had been seen displayed in the box and enquiring as to 'what was their purpose'. Their purpose was to chat with my network of union mates around the railway network when it was quiet and talk about the latest missives from union head office as well as goings-on in the Party. Which strictly speaking wasn't classed as 'railway business'.

I wasn't sure how to reply so gave Austin a ring. "Very simple Paul. Just reply to the twat saying that the list was there 'for no particular purpose' and has 'since been removed.'"

Which I did. I never heard anything more of the matter, in future keeping the list hidden on my desk under the Train Register Book.

Austin was a loyal union member and had treasured his grandfather's '40 years membership' union badge. He wasn't a left-wing militant but was tolerant of my own youthful radicalism and would occasionally buy a 'Morning Star' off me. "Just think thisel lucky tha' doesn't live in Russia, that's all I'd say", he told me. "Tha'll grow out of it", as he handed over his 30p.

He was chairman of the local branch which met each month, usually with a small handful of members whose shifts allowed them to attend. It was held in the former Guards' Room on Platform 5, which was used for ambulance classes and LDC meetings – the 'local departmental committee' – of staff reps.

That special meeting he'd called for on a warm day in June 1985 – just before the annual 'Bolton Holidays' were due to start – was different. The room was packed and people had to stand round the back of the room. Word had got about that a re-signalling scheme was on the cards.

Austin called for 'order', rapping on the table with his ancient gavel, used by generations of branch chairmen. He declared the meeting open, with a perfunctory 'welcome brothers' and said there was only one item on the agenda – the re-signalling project.

"Management have informed me that a new power-operated signalbox in Manchester is to replace all the manual boxes in our area, within the next twelve to eighteen months. Sounds optimistic to me, but anyroad...they've assured me that no signalman will be made compulsorily redundant, as there are signalling vacancies within the region. Also, the more senior men will be able to transfer to the new power box when it opens."

Austin returned to his seat and several hands shot up.

"That's all very well," said Maurice Davies, one of the younger signalmen. "I haven't got the seniority to get a job in the power box, are they expecting me to move to bloody Workington or some God-forsaken hole?"

"There are vacancies in manual boxes closer to home," answered Austin. "The Blackpool and Southport areas have plenty and you'd be near the seaside!"

"You won't catch me going into any power box," commented Alf Shillitoe. "Signalmen only come out o'them places one road – in a coffin! You can't even go for a piss without getting someone to tek ovver."

"Yes indeed Brother Shillitoe but please moderate your language in the branch room," replied Austin, putting on his sternest expression.

Other members asked about redundancy terms if no suitable vacancy could be found. Quite a few were for taking the money if the deal was a good one.

"Th'job's knackered anyway," said Brian Holmes, who'd been at Bolton No. 2 for over 20 years. "They've shut the Bury line, Halliwell goods yard has finished an' there's talk o' th' parcels depot closing. There's nowt goin' to be left. We meyt as well get eawt when we've th'chance."

Murmurs of approval ran through the meeting.

"I can't see as I disagree with Brother Holmes," said Austin. "All I'm doing is giving you the facts. An enhanced redundancy package will be offered to anyone who doesn't want to move."

The meeting closed and most of the gathering transferred to the nearby Church Inn where the conversation continued over pints of Magee's bitter beer, reflecting the mood.

The next twelve months was an unhappy time. The signalboxes that had once been immaculate, with brass instruments and lever handles polished each day, began to look shabby, the levers discoloured. The linoleum floors no longer gleamed when you walked through the door, sometimes slipping on the polish. The exception was Green Lane, which Austin kept spotless, though his mates on the other two shifts had lost interest. The animated debates over the circuit telephone narrowed down to just one item – what was going to happen come next December when the new power box was scheduled to go 'live'.

Many of the men had already decided to go for early retirement. They were guaranteed a lump sum on finishing, on top of their railway pension. That retirement bungalow in Lytham, which some had dreamed of, began to look like a possibility.

"Lucky sods!" thought most of the younger men, sick of the insecurity.

"We've been told there are lots of vacancies on the Midland Main Line, round St Albans and Luton, during the route modernisation," said Dave Entwistle over the circuit phone. "Good money, and twelve hour shifts...for about six months, and then they shut as well! What's the point of anyone moving for that?"

The decline Austin had experienced at Croal Bridge Junction came to Green Lane, like the spread of a virus. More and more white levers appeared alongside the reds, blacks, yellows and blues. Sidings closed and the branch to Darcy Lever was taken out. The gantry which once supported an array of signals looked naked, with just a couple of remaining semaphores.

Work on the new power signal box (PSB) was proceeding, with December 1985 set for the start of the transfer. Some 25 boxes in the area would go, with around 150 men 'displaced'. The PSB would employ six men per shift, adding up to about 25 in all, allowing for relief cover. Of the other 125, some had already said they were 'taking the money'. A few transferred to manual boxes around the region whilst others held out for a transfer to the new power box.

Nobody had asked Austin what his plans were. Everyone assumed he'd swallow his pride and transfer to the PSB in Manchester. They needed men with his expertise and knowledge.

When discussions started with management about where the remaining signalmen were going, they had already pencilled in Austin for the PSB on account of his seniority – and his dedication.

A meeting with management was arranged at the new regional HQ, Rail House, in Manchester with the LDC reps – Austin included – and union officials.

They went down the list of transfers and applications and when it came to 'Shorrock, A., Green Lane' the clerk was about to write in 'PSB'.

Austin stopped him. "I won't be going," he announced. "I'm taking redundancy."

Everyone around the table was stunned. "But we'd always assumed, Mr Shorrock...." stammered Joe Gorton, the Area Manager.

"Mr Gorton, as my father taught me at the start of my signalling career, never assume, always ascertain."

"You'll never get another job at your age, Austin," chipped in Dennis Bromley, one of the union men. "Think of your future – and you'll be able to retire in less than ten years with a good pension."

"I've made my mind up. This job's had it, I've had enough. I'll join the other three and a half million on the dole. There's room for one more."

Word got round the remaining signalmen who were keeping the doomed boxes operating. The circuit phone was full of rumours and speculation, the most fanciful being that Austin had finally got himself 'fixed up' – with a rich heiress who owned a mansion in Cheshire! Other more realistic suggestions included one that he'd been offered a job as volunteer signalman on one of the preserved railways. Or that he was going to use his continental passes and travel around the world.

None of the stories was true. Austin simply had nowhere to go, or so it seemed.

Most of the surviving boxes were due to be de-commissioned during December and January. Green Lane was first to go, with the changeover on the first Sunday in December. My own box – Oaks Lane – wasn't affected thanks to a quirk in the system. The new PSB at Manchester, it turned out, wasn't able to communicate with its well-established neighbour at Preston. The only way the (very highly-paid) technicians could resolve the problem was to retain a handful of traditional signalboxes that would become 'fringe boxes' and act as a buffer between the two mighty PSBs. Oaks Lane was one of them, dating back to 1848.

I was on earlies that week, finishing at 14.00. I knew Austin was on lates so on Monday evening I called round to pay my 'last respects'. It really did feel like an imminent death in the family.

I left the car down the road and climbed up to the box. In traditional railway style stamping hard on the steps so the signalman would know someone was coming. It would give them time to remove any TVs or radios which inspectors would frown on. He came to the door and saw it was me.

"Come to say a last goodbye, Austin."

"Come in lad. Like a cup o'tea?"

We chatted about old times, how I'd trained with him in my first few months after transferring from being a guard. All the daft mistakes I'd made and my failure to recognise the different tones of the block bells. He was more chatty than usual, though he looked slightly distant.

I knew it was a daft question but I asked it anyway. "What are you going to do?"

"Oh, I'll find plenty to do. Mum needs looking after more and more, she's getting increasingly doo-lally. But I've other things I want to do. I'm going to learn to play the piano, for starters and I've found a tutor who lives over Harwood way. I've always liked my music, I think you know that. Doing this job gives you a sensitive ear, though maybe not in your case!"

"Well, yes but it's amazing what sticking a bit of wood into the bell can do...but the trouble with this job, shifts and long hours, you don't get chance to develop other interests. But that doesn't explain why you decided to finish though...."

"Right. Just look out of the window – that new bloody motorway. There used to be fifteen siding roads there. Look at all these white levers. Depressing. And what was I offered? Being stuck in a centrally-heated hen coop for eight hours a day. Oh yes, the money was good but I've never been interested in 'grabbing'. I've got all I need, and my railway pension is adequate for me, even with finishing early. So I've had enough. I made my mind up a long time ago."

We chatted a bit longer, about his favourite composers and their piano works – he'd broadened his interests to include Debussy, Dvorak and many I'd not heard of.

"Well Austin, all the very best."

"Aye, same to you lad. And take my advice – you've got brains, do summat with 'em! Don't stick around with this job."

I was in the pub on Saturday night and wondered how Austin was. It was his last shift, signing on at 22.00 with a 06.00 finish.

After that, the signal engineers were scheduled to move in and rip out the guts of the signalbox and remove the remaining semaphores. The new multiple-aspect signals were already in place but covered up. Trains would be worked through by hand signalmen under special arrangements.

I was tempted to call round and see him after last orders but it would have seemed an intrusion and the place would probably be crawling with inspectors and managers anyway.

I only found out on Monday afternoon what happened that night. I was changing shifts with Dougie McKillop who was on earlies, and he told me the story.

That Saturday night the signal engineers booked to close and dismantle Green Lane were called out to another job – a signal failure near Guide Bridge, the other side of Manchester. At 6 a.m. on the Sunday morning there was no sign of anyone. As it was supposed to be the last shift, no signalman had been arranged to relieve Austin for the following eight hours. Control had assumed Austin would work four hours of overtime, allowing the signal engineers time to get up to Green Lane to start the decommissioning.

At 6 o'clock precisely Austin picked up the phone and dialled Control in Manchester.

"Hello. Control? Austin Shorrock at Green Lane. I am now signing off duty and replacing all my signals to danger."

Without waiting for a reply, he put the phone down. He then sent the bell signal '7-5-5' – 'switching out' – to the adjoining boxes at Bolton No. 2 and Croal Bridge.

He damped the fire down, swept the floor and gave the lever handles a final polish. It was 06.05 and his shift was over. He ignored the phone's constant ringing as Control tried to make contact and plead with him to stay on for a few hours.

He closed the door behind him, without a backward glance.

That weekend the West Coast Main Line was closed for engineering work and most London–Glasgow expresses were diverted via Bolton. 1M56, the Glasgow–Euston sleeper, reached Bolton at 06.15 to find that the signals south of the station were at danger. The signalman at Bolton No. 2 called him on to the signalbox window.

"I'm sorry driver, Green Lane isn't communicating – you'll have to wait further instructions."

As the morning wore on, other trains created a tail back stretching up from Salford and down from Chorley. Eventually, an on-call signalling inspector, qualified to operate the box, got to Green Lane and it enjoyed a temporary four hours' re-birth before the engineers arrived and the signals were removed and despatched to 'Collector's Corner' in London, to adorn middle class gardens in the South of England, to whom 'Green Lane' was just a nice rustic-sounding name.

Austin had stuck by the Rule Book to the end. He'd worked his shift and in the absence of relief had put back his signals to danger. With the Rule Book on his side, he'd gone down fighting.

The entry in the Train Register Book read:

Signed off duty 06.00h. A. Shorrock. End of railway service – 39 years, 6 months, 5 days

Who Signed The Book?

A classic scene: The former Lancashire and Yorkshire Railway signal box at Windsor Bridge (Salford). The armchair has seen many years' service!

I've spent the last 40 years as union branch secretary getting other people out of trouble. I've done more disciplinaries than you'll have had hot dinners – and I've had some bloody strange ones. But you want to know the strangest? I'll tell you. It happened nearly 40 years ago and there's enough water flown under the bridge for me to talk about it now. I'm long since retired so there's not much anyone can do to me. I've got my pension.

I must have represented hundreds of my members at what they used to call 'Form 1 hearings'. Disciplinaries. But this one found me in the hot seat.

What led me to getting charged happened in 1983. Until now the only people to have known anything about it are me and Jack Bracewell, former Area Manager – and he's been retired even longer than I have. He lives out Blackpool way. I promised I'd keep my mouth shut about the affair until Jack had finished and was getting his company pension. As a good union man, I've kept my word.

It was Christmas Eve 1983. I was working nights at Astley Bridge Junction; a small signal cabin just north of Bolton on the steeply-graded line to Blackburn. It's long gone of course – it shut when the branch to Halliwell Goods closed in the late '80s. It was the draughtiest box I've ever worked, stuck on top of Tonge Viaduct with only the birds and the circuit telephone to keep you company, apart from the occasional platelayer's visit – usually Derek begging a brew of tea!

We'd had plenty of rows about it on the LDC – the 'Local Departmental Committee' where we battled things out with management – usually good naturedly. Astley Bridge was one of the ancient Lancashire and Yorkshire (L&Y) boxes with facilities which could best be called 'primitive'. Heating was by an old stove that Stephenson probably invented, gas lighting and an outside toilet that froze every winter. And then that bloody draught that blew up from below, through the lever frame. Management kept telling us it was 'in the programme' for modernisation, but nothing happened.

It had its compensations. You could look across Bolton and see the dozens of mill chimneys, mostly still working then, while turning north the moors stretched out before you. And it was cosy when you got the fire going, and no-one could say you were killed for work, with just a couple of trains each hour and the occasional goods on and off the branch. Years ago it had been on a through route to Scotland. Lancashire and Yorkshire expresses joined up with The Midland at Hellifield. Well before my time. Or so I thought.

At the time, we were working short-handed. My mate Joe Hepburn had retired three months earlier and management were dragging their feet about filling the vacancy. So we were on regular twelve hours, George Ashcroft and myself. Good for the money, but not for your social life; nor, as I began to think, for your sanity.

Have you ever been to a Form 1 hearing? It's probably different nowadays but back then it probably hadn't changed since Victorian times. You sat there like a naughty schoolboy, usually accompanied by your union spokesman. If it was serious, the Area Manager would take the case and he'd read out the charge: "You are charged with the under-mentioned irregularity....etc." A clerk would be sat in the background, taking notes of the ordeal and loving every minute of it, most times.

A good union man will use every argument in the book – and out of it – to get the poor bugger on the charge as good a deal as possible. I had a better success rate than many full-time union officers. I had just one rule: I never told a lie to get a member off the hook. If you pull that one, it might work the first time, but the boss would make it bloody hard for you the next. And that next time you might have had a genuine case.

So can you imagine how I felt, with 30 years' service, including 20 as branch secretary, when I got that Form 1 addressed to me. But I'd been expecting it. And I thought I'd be up the road.

The hearing was on a Friday morning in January 1984 at 09.00, in the Area Manager's office on Bolton station. Jack Bracewell, the AM, was an old hand whom I knew from his days on the footplate. He was one of that dying breed of railway manager who'd started off at the bottom – as an engine cleaner at Plodder Lane shed – and worked his way up the ladder.

Ironically, I'd got him off his hook, years earlier, by which time he'd got booked as a driver at Bolton. He was driving a loose-coupled coal train from Rose Grove to Salford Docks and I was on duty at Astley Bridge Junction at the time, on relief. I got the 'train on line' bell from Bromley Cross box but I had an engine off the branch waiting at my starter to go back to the shed, so I couldn't give the coal train a road. He'd have to wait at my home signal, just up from the end of the viaduct.

I heard a long piercing whistle then a series of short 'crows' – the steam whistle code for a runaway. I saw the train coming down the bank, with one of the old 'Austerity' locos, passing the home signal at danger. She was away, no doubt about it. Not going that fast but enough to give that light engine a nasty surprise if she caught up with it. Just as the loco passed the box I got 'line clear' from Bolton West and I quickly offered the light engine. It was accepted and I was able to clear my starter to get the light engine out of the way. The coal train came to a halt just a few wagon lengths beyond my box.

The driver – Jack Bracewell – was quickly out of his cab and up the cabin steps. "Sorry mate – there was no holding her. Overloaded to start off with – we nearly stuck in Sough Tunnel – and that old wreck's brake wouldn't stop a push bike, ne'er mind 40 o'coal. Anyroad, put it in t'book and I'll answer for passing that home board."

Some signalmen I knew would book a driver for not having his hair combed right, but I wasn't going to get anyone into trouble if I could help it – even if he was an ASLEF man and I was NUR.

"Didn't you see?" I asked, "I pulled off for you to drop down to my starter just as you approached. Forget it." We exchanged looks and Jack turned to leave. "Thanks mate – if you're ever stuck, I'll return the favour."

I looked out of the cabin window and saw him climb back into the cab of his grimy 'Austerity', wheezing steam from everywhere but now looking calm and innocent after her wild descent from Walton's Siding. I soon got the 'train out of section' bell from Bolton West for the light engine and was able to pull off for Jack's train. The wagons shuddered and screeched and he was back on his way to Salford Docks. The guard in the brake van looked a bit ashen-faced after his experience but I got a friendly and slightly relieved-looking wave from him.

That must have been..... what? 1959? Jack had come a long way since then, getting into management somewhere down south then promoted to Area Manager back in Bolton. Poacher turned gamekeeper we used to say. And the battles we had on the LDC! But at least you knew where you were with him. He was a railwayman and knew his job, and everyone else's. That's more than you can say for most of today's managers.

That day of the hearing I broke one of my golden rules. Never go into a disciplinary hearing without union representation. We'd fought hard for that right and many genuine cases were lost

A Lancashire and Yorkshire Railway 'Highflyer' speeds a Manchester–Liverpool express over Walkden Water Troughs from an L&Y postcard c 1905.

because someone thought they didn't need any help. With me, it was more embarrassment than anything. I thought of asking Benny Jones the full-time officer, or some of my old mates on the NEC. But no, none of them would believe my story and I'd look a bloody fool. I went through that door on my tod, feeling very alone: one of the worst moments of my life.

Jack was at his desk, with the young woman clerk, Joyce Williams, sat at his side, pen in hand. She was one of the better ones, and I think she had a TSSA union card.

"Good morning Mr Hartshorn. Please sit down." Jack was looking more bloody nervous than me. And Christ! I was a nervous wreck. He read the charge: "You are charged with the under-mentioned irregularity. That on Wednesday December 24th 1983 you made incorrect entries in The Train Register Book, contrary to Signalmen's Instructions and Rule Book Section such-and-such....What have you got to say in your defence?"

I looked across at Mr Jack Bracewell, Area Manager, London Midland Region. He'd put on weight since leaving the footplate; his face was a bright red and his hair receding. Maybe down to the hard time I'd given him at LDC meetings.

But today the advantage was firmly his – though you wouldn't have thought so by the look of him. Beads of sweat rolled down his forehead, he shuffled uncomfortably in his chair. "Joyce" he blurted out… "turn that bloody heating down before we all roast." The clerk jumped up and obeyed the command. The ball was now in my court.

"Before I give you my explanation Mr Bracewell I just want to remind you that I've always been straight when I've been representing my members in front of you. And I'm going to be straight with you now – however unbelievable it all might sound."

"Of course…of course, get on with it."

"Right. I relieved my mate at 6.00pm, as you know we were on 12 hours. I was sober, you can ask George to verify that if you want. We chatted for a few minutes about what we were doing over the holiday and then George signed off.

"Could be a bad 'un" I remember him saying about the weather; the snow had already started though lucky for him he didn't live that far away. We wished each other "all the best" and off he went down the cabin steps.

He'd left a good fire; the pot-bellied stove was glowing red. I settled myself down in the easy chair, with a quiet night's shift ahead of me. I saw the last 'passenger' through at 21.30. It's in the book. The only other scheduled train that night was the empty stock for Newton Heath at about 03.00. After it had gone I had permission to close the cabin early and not re-open until the following Monday, when I was early turn at 06.00.

I made a brew and settled down with my book – a thriller, funnily enough. To be honest I probably dozed off, at least for a few minutes. I was jolted out of my snooze by a 'call attention' bell from Bolton West. I wondered what on earth it could be. I looked at the clock and it showed 23.35. I gave the '1' signal back to Bolton West and they offered me a '4' – the bell code for an express passenger train, as you know, sir. The first thing that came into my mind was that the wires were down on the main line and Control was diverting some trains for Scotland via the Settle–Carlisle Line. It happens quite often, though it was very odd that I hadn't got a circuit to tell me. Perhaps I'd been in more of a sleep than I thought and had missed the wire. I sent the signal on to Bromley Cross, got 'line clear' and pulled off – home board, starter and distant. Five minutes later I received a '2' – train on line from Bolton West. I expected to hear the roar of a diesel engine, but instead I heard the steady, slow puff of a steam locomotive, obviously labouring on the gradient out of Bolton.

All I could think was that it must have been some sort of special working back to the museum at Carnforth, routed by Hellifield. It was a strange time to run it, but what was I to know? It was snowing very heavily by now, the wind blowing the flakes against the cabin windows so you could hardly see out. The tracks were completely covered.

The headlamps of the engine came into view; she'd slowed down even more and was barely moving though sparks were coming out of the chimney like a firework display.

"Aye the fireman would have the dart in to get the fire going," said Jack reverting to his old footplate patter, quickly adding "but well, that's if there was an engine…obviously. Delete that comment, Joyce."

I continued the story.

"When the engine was almost level with the cabin the steam was shut off and the train came to a stand. I managed to open the cabin door, pushing the snow back, to get a better view. Through the blizzard I could see that it wasn't one of the usual preserved locos you sometimes get – she looked older, but well kept. The paintwork looked jet black and across the tender I could make out the words 'Lancashire & Yorkshire'.

She looked like one of those 'Lanky' Atlantics that some of the older signalmen used to talk about, when I was a train booker in my teens. 'Highflyers' they called them, with high-pitched long boilers. Very fast engines. But I couldn't recall any being saved from the scrapheap.

The coaches looked vintage too, though I couldn't see much of them through the snow. It was blowing like an arctic gale, and curious though I was, I had to shut the door.

A moment later I heard footsteps coming up to the cabin. There was a rap on the door window. I took off the snack and opened the door to what looked like an oldish man – a gnarled face with a drooping moustache and eyes like red-hot coals. His hands were pitted and scarred. This didn't look like some middle-class train enthusiast who did the occasional firing turn for the fun of it.

He walked in, shaking the snow off and carefully wiping his boots on the mat. "Short o'steam mate – they're givin' us rubbish fert burn wi't'colliers on strike."

By now I could get a proper look at him. He was dressed in old fashioned railway overalls which I'd only seen in history books. He had a very dignified appearance, reminding me of some of the old Methodist preachers I knew as a kid.

It was news to me that the miners were on strike, but that didn't click at first. It took me a few seconds before I could say anything – though I offered him a brew and asked him to sign the Train Register Book, according to rule. I'd placed collars on the signal levers to protect the train.

A few moments later more footsteps told me that his mate – the driver – was coming up for a warm as well. He looked about the same age as his fireman, slightly smaller with a long greying beard speckled with snowflakes and coal dust. He had similar overalls to his mate but wore a shirt and tie, with a shiny watch chain disappearing into his waistcoat pocket. He wore the L&Y insignia on his lapel. I remember thinking that if these two lads were steam buffs, they were certainly sticklers for historical accuracy.

The driver said, to no-one in particular, "There'll be hell to play o'er this. Runnin' short o' steam on this job, we'st booath be on th'carpet o'Monday. It's noan mi mates fault though – it's that bad coyl they're givin' us. Tha cornt wark this sort o'job, wi' nine bogies an just an hour to geet fro' Bowton to Hellifield, wi nowt but th'best coyl. Th'bosses durnt give a bugger though – they just put th'blame on th'men."

I didn't know what to think. Was I caught up in an elaborate practical joke? Or was I in a time warp? I reminded myself that I hadn't been drinking. Maybe I was still asleep and this was a very vivid dream?

That was it. I'd soon wake up and get 'call attention' for the Newton Heath empties.

But it continued. The fireman went over to the stove to warm his pock-marked hands. "Th'company thinks as it con do what it wants wi' us. It allus has done. But it's geet a shock comin'. There's talk o'one big union for all railwaymen after last year's strike. Federation 'ud be a good start. They've kept us divided for too long, grade agen grade, men agen men."

The fireman halted for a while, feeling the heat return to his hands, and then continued "Aw've waited for th'day when we'd beat the company for a long time. Aw've suffered through bein' a union man and socialist, like mony another. Moved fro' shed t' shed. Tret like dirt. Neaw there's a change comin'."

The driver explained that his mate had been victimised following his part in the Wakefield strike…I'd never heard of it, even though I'd been a union man myself for 20-odd years. I had read about something kicking off around Wakefield in the union history, but that was way, way back. The bearded driver continued the story, explaining that the strike was broken by the company using fitters to drive the engines, with passenger guards providing the route knowledge.

"Usual tale – divide an' rule!" he added. The leaders were either sacked or transferred and told they'd be married to a shovel for the rest of their working lives. No promotion.

His fireman finally ended up at Newton Heath shed, after several moves to holes like Bacup, Lees and Colne Lanky. He was still a fireman after 40 years' service with no prospect of getting booked as a driver.

But hang on, I asked myself, was I playing a bit part in some union-sponsored costume drama? I could just remember reading about a big strike in 1911, before the NUR was formed. Were these blokes having me on?

"Aye," said the driver. "There'll be changes soon, reet enough. Anyroad, Aw'll goo an' oil reawnd. Valves are starting to pop so looks like we've got steam! Good night brother, and all the best."

The fireman stayed a few moments longer and stood gazing round the cabin. "All reet these modern cabins, eh? Tha's a bloody sight better off nor us locomen. Look what we've to put up wi'!"

pointing outside to the snow-swept cab of his engine. "Still," he continued, "we know the long heawrs you lads have forced on you – sixteen hour days wi' no overtime pay." I thought of some of my mates, for whom the idea of working sixteen hours would be heaven – providing they got time and a half.

"Well friend. Aw'll geet back – she's blowin' off neaw. She'll get us up th'bank to Walton's. Sooner we're at Hellifield and relieved bi Midland men, the better. Hellifield lodging house allus does a gradely breakfast. Good neet and thanks for th'brew. Aw con tell a comrade when aw meet one."

I watched him climb back onto the footplate and start shovelling more coal into the firebox. His mate stood by the long regulator handle, lit up by the glare from the fire. A shrill high-pitched whistle pierced the blizzard and the train began to move, with a powerful exhaust cutting through the snow storm.

I turned to my desk and looked at the Train Register Book. I noticed the fireman's entry: "Detained within protection of signals. Rule 55." The signature looked like 'J.Weatherby'. If they were ghosts, they could sign their name!

I looked out of the cabin window and could just see the tail lamp in the distance. Suddenly it was gone, consumed by the blizzard. I gave a '2' – train entering section – to Bromley Cross and sent the 2-1, train out of section, back to Bolton West. The entries are in the book and they were accurate to the minute. Both were recorded at 23.55.

The phone rang. It was Ernie Woodruff at Bolton West. "What's that 2-1 tha just sent? Hasta gone daft?"

We nearly had a row. I told him he'd sent me a '4' and the train had been detained at the box. I didn't tell him what sort of train it was. Ernie denied sending the signal and said there'd been nothing on the block since the last passenger at 21.30. Anyway I thought, the proof would be when the train reached Bromley Cross. That would show who's daft, so I thought.

It never reached Bromley Cross. Ten minutes later, the signalman – Jack Seddon – rang to ask where this '4' was. There was no sign of it on his track circuit. I told him he'd been having trouble and had maybe stuck again. It's not unknown, even in the modern age, on that stretch of line.

We let another ten minutes pass and then decided something was up. As luck would have it, the Newton Heath empties from Burnley were running early and were approaching Bromley Cross. Jack 'put back' his signals and cautioned the driver of the diesel train to inspect the line ahead. The train stopped outside the box and the driver came upstairs. He reported not having seen anything.

The driver – it was Jim Woods, an ex-Bolton man I'd know for years – asked how I was. I knew what was going through his mind, that I'd had a few Christmas Eve drinks too many before signing on. I said I was OK.

I was anything but.

At 01.00, as you'll see in the book, I rang Control and asked for relief. I was no longer sure of my own sanity, and that's the truth of it. I felt faint and disoriented. Jim made me a strong cup of tea and stayed with me until the block inspector, John Brooks, arrived to relieve me and close the box.

You've heard the lot – make of it what you like Mr Bracewell."

Jack sat back in his chair – so far he nearly overbalanced. It was a few seconds before he spoke. It seemed like a very long time.

"Joyce, love, go and make us a cup of tea will you. And one for Mr Hartshorn."

The clerk got up and left the room, leaving us alone.

"Right John. This is off the record, just thee an' me. You'd had a few, right? It was Christmas. Just tell me the truth. I owe you a favour, we'll get round this somehow. Listen, if anybody else had told me that load of bollocks I'd have had 'em cleaning out the carriage shed shit house before they could say boo to a bleedin' goose. Now come on."

"I'm sorry Jack, I don't expect you, nor anyone else, to believe it. I wouldn't myself if someone else I'd been representing had told me all that."

Bracewell was quiet for several minutes. This was the man I knew. Working out a plan, weighing up the options.

"Look," he said at last. "I'll tell you what. You'd been under strain with all those 12 hour shifts. You'd had a lot of union work on too. Maybe you'd had a few pints before coming on duty and you fell asleep. Your brain wandered."

"Sure Jack. But how can anyone explain the entry in the Train Register Book?"

"Easy. We'll just say you'd been dreaming and….err…." He dried up.

"Who was it that signed the book Jack? That's not my signature. It looks like 'J. Weatherby'. Who was this character that signed the book?"

"Who signed the book….who…." he mumbled and went quiet.

He came up with another solution. "I know. There's a platelayer called 'Weatherall' isn't there?"

"Aye. Johnny Weatherall. He was on snow duty at Bolton East that night as it happens but didn't came anywhere near Astley Bridge."

"Never mind that. We can say he came up to check the points and made a balls-up of the entry in to the Train Register Book."

"Listen Jack. I'm not getting anyone else into bother over this. It's my problem, no-one else's."

"Look you awkward bugger. I owe you a good turn. And I'm going to do you one if I have to get paid up for doing it. Nowt'll happen to Weatherall, I'll see to that. Trust me."

I did. I went along with his tale. I got off with a reprimand; I was lucky. Extremely lucky. If it had been that young Assistant AM – fresh out of college – taking the case it might have been dismissal. But it didn't solve the problem for me. What had happened that night? Had I temporarily gone mad? I could never really trust myself handling traffic again until I was sure, one way or the other.

I took a few days leave that were due to me and then resumed at Astley Bridge Junction. I was on days – we were back to 8 hour shifts. On the first day a group of workmen arrived.

"You're in luck mate!" the foreman beamed. "You're getting them mod-cons you've been after all these years". The gang set to work taking out the old fittings, removing the old stove and putting in a gas heater, new toilet, modern block equipment and even new lino for the floor.

It wasn't until the following day they started work on the last job, stripping out the old linoleum floor covering, that had been polished zealously by generations of signalmen. It was a messy and disruptive job getting it out.

I was trying to complete a member's accident claim for head office when one of the lads piped up: "Hey, look at these old newspapers stuffed under the lino. Bet they're worth a bob or two!"

I went over and picked one of them up. The paper was perished and discoloured. But I could read it well enough. It was the front page of The Bolton Evening News for December 26th, 1912.

"TERRIBLE CHRISTMAS EVE TRAGEDY – EXPRESS CRASHES OVER VIADUCT IN BLIZZARD. MANY KILLED"

I read on. The train was a Scotch extra for the Christmas holidays, routed via Settle. The viaduct had collapsed at about midnight and the train careered into the river below. There was a list of casualties who had been identified so far. The catalogue of men, women and several children made heartbreaking reading.

At the end of the list was "Mr James Weatherby, the fireman of the locomotive".

Marxist to Managing Director

Northern's Kathryn O'Brien at Carlisle, October 2008, with a group of rail managers and councillors. Kathryn is now Director of Customer Services and Operations at TransPennine Express.

I was the first woman to be appointed managing director of a large railway company. Not bragging, just was. It was back in 2006 when the new franchise for Yorkshire Trains was set up. It probably helped being called 'Sam' – short for Samantha. Having a man's name sometimes gave a leg up the greasy pole in the railway industry, which was especially slippery if you were a woman. But what probably helped more than anything was that I wasn't so desperately ambitious; it was almost – but not quite – a bit of a game to see how far I could get, from being a Marxist revolutionary in Leeds, back in the '70s, to the managing director of a big private company employing 4,000 people. Some of my erstwhile lefty mates called me 'Turn-coat Turner'. Thanks, comrades!

I did Politics with Spanish at Leeds University, between 1981 and 1984. I had a fascination with the Spanish Civil War and learnt some of the language. I should say that it was a combination of theory and practice, with an emphasis more on the 'practice' – which included pitched battles with the National Front when they tried to march through some of the Asian areas of West Yorkshire. The university, at least the bit I was in, was a political hot-house back then. Several of my tutors were signed up to one or other of the far-left groups, such as the International Socialists, Workers Revolutionary Party and in a few cases the Communist Party, which we despised as 'Stalinists'.

I joined the International Marxist Group – The IMG – the year I started at Leeds. They were a kind of 'libertarian Trotskyist' outfit. Their politics were a bit more subtle than some of the far-left sects and they even encouraged different points of view, at least within the Trotskyist canon. But there was still the expectation that 'comrades' would be outside factory gates at the crack of dawn selling Red Weekly to the masses.

Leeds was a tough place in the early '80s with a growing fascist movement which regarded breaking up left-wing meetings as fair game. We didn't stand back and let it happen. We were sent ff to 'workers' self-defence' courses where we were taught basic skills in how to immobilise your opponent. As that would usually be a man, a well-aimed kick in the balls was effective!

Gerry Foley was my first love. He was a fellow student and like me a recent recruit to 'the cause'. He came from Sunderland; dad worked down the pit after coming over from Ireland in the '50s. Part of the attraction was his accent and the bright red mop of hair, which he assured me was natural.

In our second year we managed to afford a bedsit in Headingley. It was love, and lust. First time for me – Gerry was a bit sheepish about his own past, although judging by the almost hilarious failure of our first night in bed, I suspect he hadn't had many before me. But it got better.

It didn't last. He went off with a girl from Esher who had been on the same course as us. Maggie, of all names! She had some guts, I'll say that, being the secretary of the University Conservative Association in what was a hive of revolutionary student politics. Thatcher was God to her. Dad was a banker – and loaded – but I kept telling myself that had nothing to do with Gerry dumping me.

"Apart from her dad being a millionaire, what attracted you to her then?" friends might have asked. She was also quite pretty, I have to admit; prettier than me. Bitch!

I soon found someone else, Michael. Another lefty but with no pretensions about being 'working class'. Like Maggie, his parents were very wealthy, both academics and – as we used to refer to people we approved of but weren't quite like us – 'progressive'. Michael was a thoroughly nice guy and we had a good year together before he went off to Oxford to do an MA. I had no intention of being his camp follower, so we said goodbye. And I became a free agent.

I got through my final year with a respectable 2.1 and not much idea what to do next; the last thing I wanted was more academic stuff. We were being encouraged by the IMG to 'return to the class' – which meant getting some lousy job in a factory with the aim of converting the workers to the ideals of Marx, Lenin and of course Trotsky.

Somehow, it didn't appeal.

I ended up working with British Rail thanks to their 'graduate trainee' scheme. At the end of the year any graduate who wanted a career (and many didn't) would turn up for the 'milk round', where many of the big employers – private and public – would offer themselves as potential employers. It included the NHS, British Telecom, the Civil Service, some of the bigger local authorities – and BR.

Dad had spent all his life as a signalman in the Colne Valley and I knew the idea of his daughter going on the railways would appeal to him. But what sold it was the woman on the BR table handing out brochures advertising their Graduate Trainee Scheme with – believe it or not – a woman on the front cover! Back then the railways were such a male-dominated industry, the idea that BR was actually going out of its way to attract female graduates surprised me.

But I still wasn't convinced. Some of my comrades would have seen joining management, even if BR was publicly-owned, as a gross act of class betrayal. Some of them – always middle-class – as much as said so, which was a bit rich.

"Sam, you should get a job as a porter or carriage cleaner, get involved in the union. It's your class duty," one of my comrades said over a pint in The Grove after our monthly IMG meeting. "And by the way, I think it's your round..."

Sod that I thought. Getting up at four in the morning and working for peanuts wasn't my idea of even a temporary career. But what swung it was bumping into Jim Kay, one of dad's union mates and a stalwart of the local Communist Party in Huddersfield.

It was when I was doing a bit of shopping in The Merrion Centre in Leeds. My IMG mates would have derided him as a 'Stalinist', probably walking round Leeds with an ice pick tucked up his jumper ready to slaughter Trotskyist renegades. In fact he was one of the nicest guys you could hope to meet, and he always bought a copy of Red Weekly from me, probably more out of pity than interest.

"How are you doing lass? Your dad told me you'd got a good degree – congratulations! He's so very proud of you. So what are you going to do now?"

I told him I wasn't sure – my comrades were urging me to get a job in a factory or railway depot.

"They're mad. You've got talent, use it for God's sake. You're a jewel – a working class lass with brains. You could do so much to help working people in a leadership role, not sweeping out railway carriages."

I told him about the BR trainee scheme. "Aye, I've heard of it. We get some of them coming round the yard from time to time. Don't know their arses from their elbows. BR would be daft not take you on, a girl with talent who knows the railway. They've got a policy of recruiting more women into management jobs. You'd be perfect. Don't think about wasting your life in jobs which your mum and dad did their best to get out of. Get the bloody form filled in."

So I did.

I posted the completed form to BRB headquarters, at 222 Marylebone Road. I thought that was the last I'd hear of it; carriage cleaning at Neville Hill Sidings beckoned!

Four weeks later I received a letter – registered mail postmarked 'York' – to say I was being called for an interview at BR's regional headquarters – what dad called 'Main HQ'.

The first interview lasted only an hour. The main interviewer was the Assistant General Manager, very old school railway, Mister Peter Downs. Mrs Drummond, who'd been at the recruitment fair – 'Senior Personnel Officer' – was there, with a young woman taking notes.

Mr Downs seemed more interested in my railway family background than my 2.1 degree. He asked me which box dad had worked in and did a bit of reminiscing about his young days as a signalman in the East Riding. I could see Mrs Drummond getting a bit irritated at this deviation from script.

He then threw a complete wobbly into the interview.

"If you were in the signalbox and your received a '6' on the block bell, what would you do?" I immediately answered "throw all my signals to danger."

This was the 'obstruction danger' signal which all signalmen dread receiving. Dad had mentioned it once or twice when we were having the family tea – mum used to tell him off for bringing the job home with him. It probably got me through to the second interview.

"Most satisfactory, Miss Turner. You may go now, we'll be in touch."

A week letter I received another registered letter, postmarked London, asking me to attend for a two day interview at the BR Training School at The Grove, Watford. It was in three weeks' time, starting Monday morning at 11.00 a.m. prompt. A free pass, second class, Leeds to Watford via London, was enclosed.

I decided to stay with some of my IMG comrades in London on Sunday night. At first I didn't dare tell them what I was up to, but Jean Farrell wheedled it out of me over a drink in 'The Crown', a renowned Irish pub in Cricklewood, that evening. She was one of the few other working class members of the group, a Geordie though Irish ancestry. She'd been down in London for a couple of years, working for one of the unions.

"Well bloody good for you bonny lass!" she said. "It's a state-owned industry, it needs people ommitted to that, not some o' those wankers who'd like to have it privatised. Go for it!"

I got a local train up to Watford Junction the following morning, slightly hungover but looking mart in my two-piece trouser suit. The training centre was a taxi ride from the station.

The other interviewees were a mixed bunch – a fair smattering of women, and the guys I got hatting to were far from being 'posh boys' in most cases. The interview process involved some ndividual sessions as well as group interviews, which I have to say I was pretty good at.

We were all on tenterhooks though, never really being able to relax, even over drinks in the raining centre's bar that evening. But I got nattering to a girl called Heidi, who it turned out was rom a railway family as well. Dad was a guard, mum was a booking office clerk. From Wakefield; a eal Yorkshire lass.

I made a couple of life-long friends during those two days – one of them being Heidi, the other vas Bernard, probably one of the 'poshest' boys there, with a degree in Classics and a lovely, lovely guy. He lived in Reigate and confessed he'd never been further north than Watford.

We finished at 15.00h on the Tuesday, most of us saying our goodbyes at the centre, a few of us haring a cab to the station to get trains home. I went home via Manchester to avoid the rush hour n London.

Four days later the letter arrived. I had passed the interview and was asked to report for duty at Main HQ, York, at 08.30 the following Monday.

I arrived at reception and was told by the slightly imperious lady on the desk to take a seat and someone would be down 'in due course'. A couple more people whom I recognised from the Watford interview joined me, which felt nice. One of them was Heidi; it was great to see her. This was before the days we made a big show of affection, hugs and all that. We shook hands, but warmly.

I was called upstairs to meet, once again, Mr Downs. He stood up to welcome me and offered his congratulations on my entry into 'the service'. More shaking of hands.

He went through the general outline of the training, which would last up to 18 months depending on how well I did with my 'rules and regulations'. "A signalman's daughter ought to get through in a year, you obviously know your bell codes already!"

I was allocated to a station where I'd be based, though quite a lot of time would be spent at different locations around the network – Crewe, London and York. My base station was to be Harrogate, a fairly busy place but – as the station staff told me repeatedly, 'a shadow of its former self', with no expresses like 'The North Briton' to Edinburgh or King's Cross any more, just local trains to York and Leeds.

The training was nothing if it wasn't comprehensive. I had opted for a career in 'Operations' (others had gone for engineering, or HR). Sometimes we'd be thrown together, other times the 'Ops' trainees would be given more detailed sessions on signalling, passenger and freight operations, commercial duties and the like.

Gradually, some of the trainees dropped out, including Bernard.

"It's not really for me," he confessed one evening in the railway staff club at Crewe after a session on 'principles of absolute block signalling'. "Dad has offered me a job as a trainee in the family firm and I'm going for the safe option."

We kissed and I didn't see him again for a couple of years – but we kept in touch and still are, him being a director of one of the big international banks.

Sure enough I got through my training in just over a year. I received another of those rather formal letters headed 'British Railways Board' informing me that I had successfully passed my training and was to report at Huddersfield Station, as Station Manager, at 08.00 on Monday morning.

This was a stroke of luck, my dad's old territory. I'd been told that when asked where I'd like to go for my first job that trainees were never given the place they'd asked for. So I said 'London' or 'Birmingham' adding, maybe with too much emphasis, that I would prefer to avoid the North of England. The trick worked!

My first big challenge was what to wear. There was a well-established dress code for railway managers, which included the traditional bowler hat as well as a very solid Gannex overcoat which was so heavy it would stand up on its own. The idea of a woman being a manager, or anything more than a booking office clerk, was completely foreign.

Mr Downs told me to nip out and buy 'something suitable, not too showy', get a receipt and claim it back from Personnel. I opted for a rather old fashioned navy blue suit, with skirt coming just below the knees. I felt as though I looked the part.

I hadn't realised it, but I was the first female Station Manager in the North Eastern Region. The BR staff paper, Rail News, ran a feature on me and a couple of the nationals – Daily Mail, Daily Express, picked up the story. Fortunately, they hadn't found out about my 'loony left' political background but a couple of things in the Mail annoyed me, particularly the reference to spending time in the signalbox with my dad. It's true I'd spent quite a lot of time in the box when I was in my teens but I was careful not to mention it. 'Unauthorised persons' were strictly forbidden from entering the hallowed ground and dad could have got in trouble if he'd been found out. He was coming up for retirement – if any managers had noticed the story, a blind eye was turned.

Heidi Mottram, managing director of Northern, at Hull c 2008 on board a stakeholder special train. Heidi is now Chief Executive of Northumbrian Water.

Back then, the job of Station Manager was an all-encompassing role. As well as looking after a busy station, I also had responsibilities for another ten or twelve stations in the area, and ten signalboxes. There was a small train crew depot with about 20 drivers and guards. Part of my job was to go round with the wages (BR still paid out in cash in those days) which was a good opportunity to get to know the men, and a few women, on the patch.

There were some characters, including Andy, a champion fiddle player, who used to practice when he was on nights in his box at Slaithwaite. Other signalmen included at least two watchmakers, a locomotive modeller and an ornithologist. They were an educated bunch, but few of them had been to any sort of college.

Looking back, I was lucky to have been known as 'Jack Turner's lass' – it gave me quick acceptance. But I wouldn't overplay it. Most of the men and women I was working with would have given me the benefit of the doubt anyway. I showed interest, and listened to them. That's what mattered.

I spent many happy hours sitting in signalboxes up the Colne Valley or out towards Mytholmroyd, being regaled with stories of 'the old days' over mugs of tea. I could remember quite a few of the tricks of the trade that dad had showed me and soon remembered the technique of how to pull off a signal lever. Technique, not strength.

I loved my work for BR and I fitted in with their perfect profile of the thrusting female manager. I didn't mind getting up at four or five in the morning to carry out a depot visit, or get a phone call in the middle of the night when I was 'on call' to attend to a derailment. It was a real job. The hours I put in, like most of the other managers, were double what we were supposedly paid to do – but the money was good. So were the travel facilities – first class all over the network and international travel as well.

I remained resolutely single – the occasional fling and a bit of experimentation with on-line dating, but nobody special. I was married to the railway, an old cliché but true for a lot of us. Who'd want a partner who was out of bed at five most mornings and worked weekends?

If there was a down side, it was the general sense of an industry in terminal decline. The late 1980s didn't see many lines closing – Beeching had seen most of them off – but it was death by a thousand cuts. Capacity was ripped out, lines were reduced from double track to single, there was little investment in new rolling stock. Electrification virtually halted. Morale plummeted, leading to a wave of strikes.

By the early '90s it was obvious the Tories wanted to sell us off to the highest bidder – if they could find any. Some of my mates seized their chance and put in bids for some of the new franchises, or the train leasing companies. The really smart ones went for the leasing companies and made a fortune for themselves. I wasn't far enough up the ladder to be part of any bid teams, and wouldn't have wanted to be anyway. I was Area Operations Manager at the time, covering Leeds and West Yorkshire, and happy enough to carry on doing that.

Yorkshire Trains was one of the last franchises to be let and went to a management buy-out, led by Tony Rowlandson, who'd been the MD of the business when it was formed in the last months of BR. Better the devil you know, I thought. He'd started on BR as a guard and was one of the few people who'd worked up from the bottom. Yorkshire to the core and I must say I had him down as a bit of a misogynist. I once told him just that, but he just looked a bit confused. "A flippin' woman hater!" I told him.

"No lass, I love women, I've been married to one forty year now, how can I not love 'em?" I gave up trying to convert him, accepting that I was being just a tad unreasonable.

Tony called me in when the news came out that they'd won the franchise.

"Sam, sit down love. You know we've won the franchise – I don't think we had much opposition to be honest, the big players thought we were a basket case. That was to our advantage. I'd mortgaged my house to get the bid, along with a few of the other lads. The missus was bloody furious when she found out but she won't be complaining now....Anyway, we've got the mobilisation team geared up to take us through to the start of the franchise. I'm picking my top team."

There was a slight pause. God, I thought, I hope he's not going to offer me something in HR or Marketing.

"You're a bloody good operator and the lads trust you. You can sit down in the messroom and have a brew with them, without being patronising. That's good. So, how would you feel about being our Operations Director? It would mean a seat on the board, a lot of trips to London to see the fucking civil servants, attending lots of industry groups. But most of all you'll have to make this railway run as it should do. You'd have my full support. So what d'you think?"

Well, I thought I'd like to give him a great big kiss. I hope I didn't show it.

"Wow, that's great Tony. I'm delighted to accept."

"You've made my day. Thanks love. From now on you'll be invited to board meetings and you will officially take over on March 1st, vesting day, when the new franchise starts. Owt else you want to know?"

"No, I don't think so Tony, just need a bit of time to let it sink in."

"Aren't you going to ask about the money?"

"Well to be honest I hadn't thought, presumably a bit more than what I'm on now?"

"Quite a lot more, but there'll be a letter in the post with the formal offer."

I started the following Monday. Our current Ops Director, Dennis Cox, had already said he was taking early retirement and would finish before March 1st. He had leave to take so it was a very quick handover.

The new franchise specified various changes but we were left in no doubt by the civil servants that it was to be 'steady state'. Some modest changes here and there but nothing major; no big new projects.

It was a different job from being an area ops manager. Less ops and a lot more meetings on finance, HR issues and the like. We all had to learn a lot, quickly. But we managed. Our paymasters – Government, through the Strategic Rail Authority – weren't easy to work with, though one or two were OK and knew their railways. The message was "run the trains to time, don't spend any money, avoid any bad news stories."

The first few meetings we had down at Victoria Street – the SRA's offices near Westminster – went well. We were meeting our three targets. In fact, after a few years it was clear we were doing better than anyone expected and making quite a bit of money.

The quarterly board meeting for April 2005 proved a turning point. There was a three-line whip; all directors had to attend.

Tony was looking nervous, not his usual self. He was normally relaxed and full of repartee before we started board meetings.

"OK, let's make a start. Colleagues. I'll get straight to the point. We've been doing well. So well that a few of the big transport groups have been sniffing around us looking for a possible sale. First Group, Go-ahead, and some foreign outfits including Spanish Railways – Renfe – in Madrid, and Deutsche Bahn. I've had Ernie, our Finance Director, have a look at each of them – obviously all are very much initial expressions of interest. But the Renfe one stands out in terms of a good deal for us, as the shareholders. But also for our staff. Most of you will know that Renfe is state-owned and has started showing an interest in foreign contracts. They've won a few small jobs in Germany but this would be their first venture in the UK. They've promised a free hand to a UK-based top team, as long as we can deliver our targets. So what do you think?"

There was an initial silence. One or two of the guys, such as Ernie, were well aware of the situation and word had got around that this was on the cards. Most of us didn't particularly want to own a railway company; we wanted to run trains, and make a good fist of it. But selling had its attractions, especially to some of my co-directors who were coming up for retirement soon and would become overnight millionaires.

The discussion was unusually low-key. For our different reasons, we all agreed it was worth exploring further. The decision was to continue discussions with Renfe but remain open to other offers. The meeting closed half an hour early, after being told in no uncertain terms to keep this strictly confidential.

Which, if anyone knows the railway, is asking the impossible. I don't know who spread the gossip - not me! - but it was soon doing the rounds of every messroom in Yorkshire. There were the predictable jokes about paella in the staff canteens, maracas issued to the guards instead of a whistle and plenty more like it.

The sale was approved by the SRA; Ernie and Tony had managed to negotiate an even better deal than had been originally offered. From November 1st 2005 we would become a wholly-owned subsidiary of Renfe (Europe) Ltd.

A lot of people - including our own guys - assumed this would lead to big changes. In fact, the difference it made to running trains in Yorkshire was nil. 'BAU' as Tony used to say; business as usual. The changes were at the top. Tony was 63 and couldn't wait to get his hands on the pay-off. Several other directors were in much the same boat and there would be a need to get some fresh talent onto the executive board.

Madrid had said that we would have a free hand in selecting everyone except for the MD. They wanted to see five or six names including external candidates - senior people in other train companies - as well as some of our own people. Tony's last job was to sort out a list and send out invitations to potential candidates. Out of a list of 12, eight responded positively. Within the company there was Jimmy O'Rourke, Engineering Director, Anne Harrison, HR Director...and me.

Why? Well, I'd come this far, why not. I knew how to run a railway, I liked my job. And there was a slightly cheeky side of me that thought it would be a bit of a laugh, being MD of a company employing 4,000 people, owned by the Spanish state! My own personal revenge on Franco - a lefty female running their trains. He'd turn in his grave.

Being relaxed about whether you wanted a job or not always seemed a really good position. And having a smattering of Spanish did me no harm at all. The interviews were held in York, in Main HQ, chaired by Tony but with the Renfe boss, Dr. Rodolfo Villa, clearly in charge. He had gravitas and a touch of elegance.

I bumped into him - literally - in the corridor, as I was coming out of the Ladies. He immediately apologised - in Spanish. I replied likewise and we had a nice little chat before he said he had an important meeting to attend, which included interviewing me, though neither of us realised it.

I was the third person to be interviewed and he gave me a broad grin as I came in the room, but didn't allude to our previous meeting outside the Ladies toilet.

Tony introduced Dr Villa and the other members of the panel, all of whom I knew. It was an all-male line-up.

"Samantha, we'd like you to say a bit about your railway experience and how you think you could make a difference as MD of Yorkshire Trains (Renfe) Ltd. You've ten minutes."

I started off with a few words about my dad and how he'd inspired my interest in working for the railway. How I'd built up a wide range of experience in railway work - not just operations but also in HR, aspects of engineering and in being the 'public face' of Yorkshire Trains (a role that Tony was never keen on). I wanted Yorkshire Trains to be a successful business, a vibrant and important part of the Yorkshire economy; an operator that our men and women felt proud to work for; a railway that our customers liked and respected.

I probably waffled on a bit but they seemed to like it. Dr Riva asked me about my approach towards the unions - a powerful force on the railway. My TSSA membership had lapsed but I got on OK with the reps and the full time officers. I said as much and told them that if I was appointed I'd want to have a positive and friendly relationship with all the unions, but not to act as a doormat for them.

"Doormat? please explain," asked Dr Villa.

"Something that people are happy to tread their shit on." I immediately regretted saying that, interview nerves, but sod it.

"Ah! I apologise, my English vocabulary is far from perfect but now I see exactly what you mean, very nicely put. Thank you."

I fielded a few more questions about the role and my competency. The days when I'd have been asked about child care were over and I felt I'd been given a fair hearing and done the best I could.

"Thanks Sam, we've a few more candidates to see and we'll be in touch when we've made a decision," Tony said.

I got up to leave and Dr Riva said "Mucho gusto en conocerte."

I smiled and left; it was nice to meet him as well, but I didn't over-egg it by replying in Spanish. I needed a brew.

My phone rang later that evening, I was at home having a hastily thrown-together egg on toast while I watched the news. It was Tony.

"Well lass, you've made a good impression on Dr Villa. You've got the job!"

The egg on toast fell off my lap and onto the carpet, to cries of "Oh fucking hell!" which probably wasn't what he was expecting to hear.

"No, sorry, I've just knocked my tea onto the floor Tony. That's absolutely fantastic. I'm really, really pleased…"

"Well pop in tomorrow morning and we can have a chat about the handover. And I have to tell you the decision was unanimous."

It was agreed that Tony would retire on March 31st, 2006. I'd take over on April 1st which a few of my pals thought was ominous, but what the hell.

Dyan Crowther, then Commercial Director at Northern, now MD of HS1 and recently awarded the OBE, in conversation at Huddersfield c 2009.

One of my first engagements was the annual dinner at the National Railway Museum, pretty much on my doorstep in York. It brought together most of the 'great and good' of the railway industry, mostly men but with the odd girlie sticking out like a sore thumb. I put on my best dress and a splodge of make-up.

It was an eventful evening. The after-dinner speaker was Geoff Kelly, the secretary of state for transport and one of the more right-wing members of Tony Blair's cabinet. He'd upset the unions by refusing to nationalise the railways and they decided to mount a show of force outside the event to make their point.

It was a bit rough and tumble but I'd been involved in a lot worse – on the other side – in my student days. We managed to push our way through and get to the reception. I glanced through the table plans – I was on Table 2 as an 'honoured guest'. Scanning through it I saw a 'Gerald Foley' representing Everbrook Train Leasing Co. Interesting. Surely not the same Gerry?

I went over to the table and sure enough there he was, he'd kept his red hair but had put on weight. He spotted me as I came round to the table with my glass of wine.

"Sam – bonny lass! How great to see you! I nearly emailed to see if you were coming to this do.

"You've come a long way from our days in the IMG."

"Well so have you by the look of it, what's this on your name badge – Director of Corporate Affairs – Everbrook Leasing'?"

"Aye well, I suppose we've both become traitors to the working class. Maggie – you might remember her – through her dad got me a nice job in finance, down in London. Thought I'd stick it for a year or two but the money was bloody amazing. I packed the Trot stuff in, it was going nowhere and most of the so-called 'comrades' sold out well before me."

"So are you still with that Tory girl you left me for? Maggie?"

"Well, sorry about that pet. But well, we stayed together a few years, it was OK, but she actually ditched me. For a lass would you believe? So maybe it's a draw."

I nearly spilt my glass laughing. "By the 'eck Gerry, that's wonderful. I always thought there was more to Maggie than met the eye."

"Aye well, it was a long time ago. I've been with Susan fifteen years now, two kids, nice big house in Surrey. Can't complain."

"Well, like you say Gerry, we've both moved on. I still think it was worth it though – standing up against racism, fascism, supporting Mandela when Thatcher just regarded him as a terrorist. I never had much time for the Marxist theory, but we were right on some issues."

"Mebbe. I've voted Tory for the last ten years, probably Maggie's influence, I don't know. But Labour under Blair hasn't exactly brought in a workers' utopia."

We had an enjoyable evening, wouldn't put it higher than that. He was good company and we swapped a few stories about battles with the National Front and the police. I think the other members of our table were a bit surprised and kept the conversation strictly to railways.

"Well pet, it's been great seeing you again. Give me a shout if you're down in London and I'll take you out for lunch, on the house."

"That might be construed as inappropriate lobbying Gerry, seeing as we lease your rather over-priced trains. But it would be nice to have coffee."

We parted with Gerry giving me a gentle peck on the cheek.

A few weeks later the RMT union announced it was taking strike action over a pay dispute among our guards. We'd offered them a decent enough package after a long negotiating session with Craig Harrison, the union organiser. It was put to a ballot and the members rejected it, which pissed me off. A one-day strike was announced, with more to come if we didn't up the offer. We were told by the SRA that they wouldn't pay for any increase we offered. Doing it unilaterally would make the business unviable.

"Sorry love," Craig said on the phone. "I thought it was a good enough offer but some of the hot-heads at the bigger depots like Leeds and Sheffield weren't for having it and fancied a few days off work. Some of those Trots on the local committee have been stirring it."

On the first day of the strike a handful of trains ran. I'd a meeting in London and got a late afternoon train back to York. I walked off the station to be confronted by a crowd of RMT activists and assorted hangers-on waving banners demanding 'Pay up Yorkshire Trains' and 'Nationalise the Privateers'.

Some of the group spotted me and shouts of 'Turncoat Turner' went up. There was a bit of jostling, fairly good-natured. I was just emerging from the melee when I saw a face I recognised.

It was Maggie, the Tory girl. She was shouting through a loudspeaker "What do we want? Nationalise the trains! When do we want it? Now! Now! Now!"

She saw me and put the megaphone down.

"Well – Sam! How are you? Talk about role reversal, eh?"

"You're telling me. And funnily enough I bumped into Gerry Foley the other week, who's now a director of a train leasing company – the epitome of the capitalist railway!"

"Really? Doesn't surprise me though. But good luck to him. He probably told you I became a 'les', as he called me?"

"Well, yes, but I don't think he's bitter..."

"He was then. But anyway, I think we've done our bit for today and the struggle can wait while tomorrow. How about a drink?"

We went next door to The Royal York and sat down in the lounge.

"Well, this is the sort of place my dad would have liked," said Maggie, looking round. "Very posh. Select."

Some of the other residents looked over their shoulders at what they'd call this 'rent a mob' activist with bright red dyed hair, bedecked with badges and still carrying her RMT placard demanding 'Railway Workers Need a Pay Rise'.

Maggie told me that she'd got a job as a guard in Sheffield a couple of years ago, partly to atone for her middle class upbringing – said with a bit of irony – but more because she just liked trains. I warmed to her.

We talked about the old days at Leeds and the conversation inevitably strayed to the potentially difficult topic of ex-boyfriends.

"Oh yes, Gerry was a nice lad but not really for me, a bit straight-laced in a funny sort of way. I played the field, men and women. And it was quite the thing to 'be gay' back then at uni. I had a great time. Had to keep it quiet from dad though."

"So when did you join the revolutionary cause?" I enquired, sipping my glass of Shiraz.

"Oh, I never joined anything, the SWP tried their best to recruit me though. I became politicised not that long after Gerry and I split. I could see what the world was doing to dad, who was a decent man and as much trapped in the system as any shopfloor worker. The bank was taken over by the Americans and they made his life hell. I think becoming a socialist was a way of me saying 'fuck the lot of you'."

"He died of a heart attack and mum ended up in a care home, completely off her head. At heart I've always been an anarchist – even when I was a Tory! Sorry, I'm getting pissed I know. But the state has never done us any favours, BR was no workers' paradise, why go back to that?"

We stayed in the bar for far too long and got splendidly drunk. We worked out a plan for what we called 'A People's Railway'! Run by the people who actually knew about trains. Idealistic shite maybe, but other ways of running the trains haven't been a rip-roaring success.

"And the railway will still need people like you, Sam, though don't expect to get the sort of money you're on now. A workers' wage for all managers."

"Maggie, give me a hug. You're wonderful. One last drink: To the revolution!"

"The revolution!" Maggie responded, before slumping into her chair.

I carried her to the taxi rank and took her home.

A Letter from Mrs Makant

Blackburn driver Abraham Tattershall ('Ab Tat') reflects on life in the cab of his class 25 locomotive.

"It's either Mister Makant or Driver Makant t' thee."

The entire signing-on point, crowded with guards and locomen on a busy Monday morning, went quiet. The young manager immediately wished he'd picked on someone else to exercise his new-found authority. Ezra Makant was the crustiest of the old-hand drivers at Blackburn depot and the established management gave him a wide berth. "And if tha wants me to move that engine, it'd help to say 'please'."

Apart from inbred awkwardness and cunning – talents shared by many of his contemporaries who'd started on the railway back in the '30s – Ezra had one special characteristic: obsessive inquisitiveness. It probably began with the great interest many railwaymen took in 'the Sunday List', as well as checking who was working their rest day. Fights had been known to break out when one man suspected another of doing him out of a Sunday. The roster clerks were old and wise enough to make sure Ezra got his Sundays in, so he gradually broadened his surveillance activities to include everyone at the depot. It became a sort of pastime.

You'd normally find Ezra sitting in the messroom, just by the door, ready to pounce. That's if he wasn't driving trains – a sort of extra-curricular activity for Ezra. He'd casually peruse any paper he could find lying around, just visible through a cloud of cigarette smoke.

At first sight, he looked innocuous. The door would open and Ezra with leopard-like slyness would spring the trap. "Whod art doin'?" was the usual opening gambit. After that, if the victim fell into the trap and responded, he would pile in: "What time art' on?", "wheer's tha bin?", "who wi'?" until the poor bloke was crying for mercy. Some of the lads became converts to reincarnation – Ezra must have been a throwback to the days of the Spanish Inquisition.

Ezra's face suggested a hard life. It was thin and drawn, heavily lined and set off by sparse wiry hair. When he spoke, the effort seemed Herculean. His eyes would almost close as he pulled his face into a grimace, while he took the fag out of his mouth, normally a permanent fixture.

His dress was in keeping with his looks. Winter or summer it was the same 'company' overcoat – at least three times too big, acting as a sort of bell tent over his meagre frame. He swore by the old railway overcoats, refusing to countenance the more stylish British Rail corporate image. He was a 'Lanky' man to his core. His boots were of a similar vintage to his coat, although he made an occasional concession by having them re-soled. Tradition has it that old railwaymen used to take great pride in having their boots polished. At one time it was even part of the Rule Book that company 'servants' would be expected to turn up for duty promptly, 'with boots polished'. If that was so, it was a tradition that passed Ezra by; he had a tendency to treat the Rule Book's provisions as optional anyway.

Don't get the impression that Ezra lacked human warmth, though it could be hard to penetrate. He loved a joke, although usually at someone else's expense. A favourite was to torment guards by uncoupling the engine from the rest of the train, after the guard had laboured long and hard to get the train ready. When he got the 'tip' from the guard at the back of the train he'd set off, minus his train, stopping a few wagon lengths further away. When the guard came panting down to the engine Ezra would lean out and enquire "Hast fergeet fert' hook on, cock?"

I had my share of Ezra's jokes, though when I once worked with him on a long-distance job – to Carlisle – a different side to him emerged. The train was fully-braked so the brake van wasn't necessary and the guard was expected to ride in the back cab of the loco. Most drivers on 'single manned' jobs welcomed the company and were happy for the guard to ride in the front cab, though Ezra was picky who received this honour. I was one of them.

After the initial enquiries about my 'doings' – which could range from other drivers I'd been with through to some quite intimate details of my domestic life – the conversation moved on to wider things. His knowledge of his native East Lancashire was encyclopaedic. He was full of anecdotes about old Burnley characters, the Pendle witches, Chartist riots and lots more. With a bit of prompting from me – a clever bit of 'turning the tables' I thought – he began to open up about his own life. He'd started as a cleaner at the age of 13 at the small Colne L&Y shed ('Cown Lanky').

At the age of 20 he moved a few miles down the line to Rose Grove to get a fireman's job. Then came the big move. It was wartime and the company was short of firemen on 'The Midland' at Derby. He signed on at Rose Grove on a Thursday morning in February 1941. The foreman handed him a letter, which he still carried with him in the original envelope:

Fireman E. Makant
Rose Grove

Transfer Arrangements: Arrange to report at Derby (Midland) 9.00 a.m. Monday 6.2.41

• *F. Hardcastle, District Loco Superintendent, Accrington*

That gave just four days to get packed, move and find lodgings.

"Th'company towd me there were a bed for me in t'lodgin' heawse which ud do me for a week or two, but it were a mucky 'oyle".

Some of his mates were sent further south to the big London sheds, which were targets of the regular bombing raids.

"Derby got its share of Adolf's bombing but nowt were as bad as what London geet. Aw con remember firing a '3F' deawn to Cricklewood wi' a load o'coyle. We were put inside at Bedford in t'middle o't'neet and we could see London lit up, forty mile away. Never sin owt as freetenin. Th'bobby said we'd be here a few minutes – it were mooar like five heawrs. We got relief and went whom to Derby on t'cushions. Aw signed off wi' sixteen heawrs in."

Ezra met his future wife on Leicester station. He was trying to get back to Derby after getting 'relief' from Kentish Town men on a passenger job. Iris had been visiting her sister in Leicester. They shared a compartment and Ezra put aside his youthful shyness and asked if she would like to see a film the following Saturday. Three months later they were married!

After the war ended a vacancy for a passed fireman came up at Accrington. It was near home and Iris had grown to like East Lancashire on their trips up north to see Ezra's parents in Colne. They both agreed on the move and Ezra got another summary command when he signed on one morning – to report for duty at Accrington the following week.

Accrington was a busy depot – the 'A' shed for East Lancashire, superior to Rose Grove which was merely '24B'. Everything on the railway has its pecking order. Most of the work was local passenger jobs though they did have one turn working the morning Colne–London to Stockport and some excursions to Blackpool, Southport and even as far as Llandudno. By 1960 the shed had turned over to diesel traction, with the remaining steam locos transferred to Rose Grove and Lower Darwen. Ezra and his mates were glad to see them go at first. He started to put on weight. Driving diesel multiple units to Manchester, Colne, Preston and Bacup was a sedentary occupation compared with firing a Lanky 'A Class' up Baxenden Bank.

Tom Kelly, spent most of his footplate career at Rose Grove shed, transferring to Blackburn when the depot closed. Pictured on his last day before retirement, c 1977.

What the Accrington men hadn't counted on was the impact of Dr Beeching. His infamous report of 1963 recommended the closure of most of the network around East Lancashire including the fast route from Accrington to Manchester via Bury, the Bacup branch and many more.

By the late 1960s there was less and less work for Accrington's diesel fleet and rumours started to fly, often initiated by Ezra. The fewer drivers remaining the more overtime there'd be, as well as extra rest day working and Sundays.

Yet unlike many of Ezra's 'news' items, this rumour became true. March 1965 saw the depot close, with work transferring to Newton Heath in Manchester, which had a brand-new diesel depot just waiting to take 'Accy's' work. The men had the option of transferring to Rose Grove or Lower Darwen, ironically returning to steam work. Some of the older drivers took the money and retired, not wanting to exchange their smart green diesel driver's uniforms for their steam-age overalls. Ezra, contrary as ever, opted to go back on 'the footplate', returning to Rose Grove.

It was only three years before the writing was on the wall for Rose Grove – and the end of steam. The depot was to close on 6th August 1968; most men would sign on at Rose Grove station for a while but rumour had it that everyone would transfer to Blackburn by the end of the year. It took a bit longer, but everything does on the railway.

The yards at Rose Grove – the Up and Down Grids, once some of the busiest in Lancashire, became quieter as the pits closed and there was no longer the demand for power station coal from Yorkshire to Huncoat, Padiham and Whitebirk.

By 1972 Ezra, with the remaining Rose Grove men who hadn't taken the money, was signing on at Blackburn depot. It was a forced marriage of Lower Darwen men, but like some such arrangements it worked. Nobody liked the extra travel from Burnley to Blackburn but a night-time 'staff train' was provided to get men to and from work.

The move to Blackburn gave Ezra and his Rose Grove mates the chance to learn the road to Carlisle – 'The Midland', via Settle. There was a lot of work that way during and after electrification of the main line over Shap. Most of the slower freights were routed via Blackburn and Settle and the depot enjoyed a brief 'golden age' of long-distance freight work and the occasional diverted passenger job.

The second time I was booked on a Carlisle job with Ezra was to be our last. I was moving to a different grade, and Ezra was retiring. This was his last turn and I felt honoured to be with him.

We signed on at 06.00 on a fine October morning to work the 'salt train' from Winsford, which carried about a thousand tonnes of rock salt for Scottish roads and factories. Our train, with the usual English Electric Class 40 diesel at the front, was waiting for us on the through road. I rang Preston Power Box from the signal and we quickly got a green with 'the feather' to take us across onto the 'down' line and through Blackburn Tunnel. We branched off at Daisyfield Junction and started the first of our 'long drags' up to Wilpshire.

The run through the Ribble Valley, with the sun just peeping through, was a delight. Pendle Hill was watching our progress as the loco got stuck in to the sharp climb from Chatburn to Rimington, immortalised in a great hymn by local man Francis Duckworth. The words seemed appropriate:

Jesus shall reign where'er the sun
does its successive journeys run,
his kingdom stretch from shore to shore,
till moons shall wax and wane no more.

Ezra knew it off by heart and he even attempted a few lines before the cough stopped him.

"These fags 'ul bloody kill me one day," he spluttered before shutting off power as the train rolled through Gisburn – then lighting up another.

He carried on with a few entertaining tales of witches and 'boggarts', with a bit of prompting from me. "Tha's gerrin wurse nor me fer axing questions," he said, in a rare moment of self-awareness.

We got a clear road through Hellifield and 'got 'em swinging' in the dip through Long Preston, before hitting the climb from Settle Junction. It was here, a few months earlier, that another ex-Rose Grove man, Manny Kay, had come to grief on the same job. He took the junction at high speed, not realising he had a 'hot box' on one of the front wagons. The whole lot came off, with only the loco remaining on the rails.

We passed Settle and the pace settled down to a steady 20 mph. The views across Ribblesdale and up to Whernside, Penyghent and Ingleborough were magnificent. I'd brought my camera and got a few photos with the cab window down and even managed to sneak a couple of Ezra, to his consternation.

"Aw durnt even let Iris tek picthurs o'me!" he rasped. "Tha'll brek th' bloody camera!"

We got relieved at Carlisle by a Scottish crew – 'Caley men' to Ezra, although the Caledonian Railway had ceased to exist in 1923. But maybe the Polmadie men approved of the deep blue livery of our engine, albeit a much more mundane loco than the 'Cardean' that once graced the line.

That day we were booked 'home passenger' via Preston. I filled the brew can in the station messroom and brought it out as our train rolled in, with a modern 'leccy' on the front and familiar Preston men ready to take it over.

"Aw thowt they'd retired thee bi neaw!" Jack Duckworth shouted over to Ezra.
"Three heawrs fert goo!" he replied. "So durnt be late."
We settled down at a free table and tea was poured. Ezra seemed a bit more thoughtful than usual, gazing out of the window as we passed Penrith, Thrimby Grange and Shap Summit. He'd done over 40 years 'for the company' as everyone still called BR. I'd done just three and was moving on to new pastures as a supervisor in Liverpool.
"Aw tell thi cock, aw'll be glad to be eawt o' this lot. Railroad as aw knew it 's finished. Aw've bin pissed abeawt from pillar to post these last forty year. Management today couldn't run a bloody chip shop, ne'er mind a railroad. Like that daft bugger aw tore a strip off. Tha cornt run this lot wi a degree – tha needs skill and experience, years of it. Aw knows tha's geet a degree in summat but at least tha con use a shuntin' pow."
This was probably the nearest I ever got to a compliment from Ezra, but it stayed with me. I have to admit I wasn't the most expert of railwaymen in the use of a shunting pole but I managed.
We were arriving into Preston, passing Barton and Broughton before the brakes came on. "Bloody railway. Hope aw never see another train," he ended, with a degree of finality as we rolled into Platform 4.
On our rattling diesel train back to Blackburn he became a bit more positive, saying he was hoping to write a book about his home town of Colne. "They fergeet that we've eawr own history," he said. "They cawd Nelson 'Little Moscow' an' even th'women were feighters for th'union an' th'vote."
He'd get himself down to the local library, but first he'd finish off that decorating he'd been promising Iris.
We signed off together, at 15.45.
Ezra was going out of the door and he turned round, looking a bit sheepish. He took my hand. "Good luck cock" – and he was away, running over the track like a mountain goat, to get his train back to Colne.

Three months later I received a letter postmarked 'Nelson and Colne'. It was from Mrs Makant – Iris.

Dear Mr Salveson,

I am sorry to bother you. My husband, Ezra, passed away last month after a sudden heart attack. He was up some ladders wallpapering. I'd told him not to but you probably know what he was like. I remember him telling me you took some pictures of him on the railway and I would be very grateful if you could send me a couple of copies for which I will of course pay you. Ezra never let me take any photos of him, he always said he was too ugly. It would be nice to have a few photos to remember him by.

Yours faithfully,
I. Makant (Mrs.)

First Day at the Loco Works

A couple of Works' 'characters' in the Chain Shop, Horwich, March 1983.

Horwich was a 'railway town'. It built locomotives, some of the best in the world. It trained the likes of Nigel Gresley who designed 'Mallard' and 'Flying Scotsman'. Today it's described on road signs as a 'historic railway town'. It isn't a railway town any more – just an 'historic' one.

The coming of the Loco Works transformed a sleepy mill village into a large industrial town of 20,000 people. Its period as a railway town lasted for just under a century, from the mid-1880s to 1983.

When the Works opened it was one of the most advanced railway engineering plants in the country. The Lancashire and Yorkshire Railway was proud of its new factory and made sure its workers had company loyalty instilled into their bones. There wasn't much of that left by the time I started working there, in 1974.

My flat was on Lee Lane, the main street of the old town. It was furnished, with a comfortable settee that you had trouble getting up from. There was a kitchen with a gas cooker and a small dining table for two and an even smaller bedroom with a double bed squeezed in. Looking out of the bedroom window you could catch a glimpse of Rivington Pike rising up in the distance.

I'd left university with an undistinguished 'lower second'. I'd made half-hearted attempts at getting a job as a graduate trainee in local government – I even got an interview for a housing officer job in South Shields. But I lacked motivation. All I needed was a job, anything would do. I could maybe get involved in workplace politics and join a union.

I rang a couple of places to see if they had anything going for unskilled labourers, as opposed to failed political scientists or critical sociologists. I tried a couple of places in Bolton and got nowhere. In desperation I rang British Rail Engineering Limited, Horwich, as it described itself in the phone book. 'Horwich Loco' as everyone knew it. I knew the pay was rubbish but it was handy for the flat.

"Yes, we're taking on labourers. It's not easy work I have to tell you, but there is a bonus scheme, overtime and railway travel facilities after you've been with us for more than six months. You'll start on £4 a week."

He might have added that most don't last that long; many jacked the job after a week. "Come down for your medical tomorrow morning and bring some references."

References? What were they recruiting? Atomic scientists?

That evening I went round to see my dad, still living in his council house in Great Lever where he'd been for 30 years. He'd lived on his own the last four. Mum had gone off with 'Slimy Jack' Heaton, the local greengrocer and they were living in a bungalow near Lytham St Annes.

I told dad about my new career. He thought I'd gone mental. He'd worked all his life in Walker's Tannery and had hopes for his lad becoming 'summat in an office', at least. Maybe a teacher. Instead, I was starting at the Loco Works, lowest of the low. What a kick in the teeth it must have been, after he'd never had chance to do anything but work in a foul-smelling, soul-destroying lime pit.

"Tha'll do what tha wants to do," he told me, gazing into the fireplace. "You always were headstrong. Like your mum. Y' tek after her mooar than me. But I'll give you six months and tha'll be regrettin' it."

When I turned up at the gatehouse the next day I was sent down to the Personnel Office and was given a form to fill in by one of the clerks. I'd got some paperwork from a summer job I did the previous year and thought I'd blag the rest. The clerk was a nice enough bloke. I told him the truth about university, more or less. I said I couldn't manage on a student grant and had decided to leave and just wanted something short-term to tide me over. I didn't say I was interested in a workers' overthrow of capitalism, seeing my employment at his shithole factory as a small step in that direction.

I was sent for my medical and got the all clear. I was to start on Monday morning, 18th May at 07.30. 'David Horrocks, shopman category 1'.

I arrived in good time. There was a group of ten of us gathered at the gate house. Most were signed up for the Foundry, though for some reason I was to be sent to the Spring Smithy, at the far end of the Works. First, we were taken into the Personnel Office to sign more forms.

"Right, sign these – your contract of employment with BREL; your membership of the Pension Fund – and this, your union membership. You've got to be a member of either the engineering union or the railwaymen's union. Which one do you want?"

It turned out that the NUR – National Union of Railwaymen – was a few pence a week cheaper than the engineers, so I opted for that. You couldn't afford to be too principled on £4 a week!

I was taken down to the Smithy by one of the 'green card men' – mostly old blokes who had come off their proper job through ill-health or an accident and just buggered about the works doing nothing much. My escort was Fred Ramsbottom, who spent most of his time brewing up in the gatehouse. He was Horwich born and bred; locomotive oil ran through his veins instead of blood.

"Right, come this way lad. Hasta bin here afoor?"

"No, I've heard about it though, my uncle worked on the railway as a driver and he used to bring locos in for repair. Sometimes used to let me have a ride in the cab."

"Well tha were lucky. This is weer they used to build 'em. It oppened in 1886. Befoor then Horwich were nowt but a little village. We don't do any loco work no mooar though, that finished in '65. It's all wagons and coaches now, though we've started repairing some electrics from Liverpool way. Reet – over theer it's th'Paint Shop. Let's walk through here and ah'll show thi a few mooar sights as we go along here. Tha knows what this road's called? 'The Golden Mile'. It's over a mile long and runs from one end o'th'works to t'other. It's a bit of a joke like."

It didn't look like any holiday camp I'd seen before, that was for sure.

We walked past the Boiler Shop and Machine Shop, before Fred took me into the Erecting Shop where the main job of building locos once took place. "It's cawd th'Wagon Shop neaw, aw they do is mend bloody wagons. A bit different from when I worked 'ere, overhaulin' big steamers. Noisy too. That's why mi 'earin's buggered."

On the jigs in the Spring Smithy, Horwich Loco Works, 1983

Fred got plenty of 'ow do's' and 'aw reets' as we walked through the shop. Everyone knew him. He'd started here as an apprentice in 1938 but within a couple of years was called up for the army. He spent the next five years in the Lancashire Fusiliers – Egypt, Burma and other hell-holes. When he was de-mobbed there was a job waiting for him back at the Loco Works. He did another two years of his apprenticeship and was taken on as a boilersmith.

I tried asking him about his war-time experiences but he just answered in monosyllables. "Aye" and "Appen" and "Ah suppose so..." He was a lot more talkative about the Works though. Just like my dad who'd never talk about the War.

"It were a bloody noisy owd place then, that's why aw wear this hearin' aid. We had to caulk th' locomotive boilers – noisy, and heavy. But it were skilled work. If you didn't get th' boiler stays reet, th' engine wouldn't steam."

We emerged from the Wagon Shop and walked through the Foundry, all part of my conducted tour.

"This is a dirty 'ole, think thisel lucky they've not sent thi' 'ere lad."

It was a hot, noisy place. Most of the work seemed to be making brake blocks for the wagons, using castings that went round on a sort of belt. Unlike other parts of the works, there were a few black faces here. Mostly Asian lads but a few Africans too. You didn't have to be time-served to work in the Foundry. The chance of getting an apprenticeship if you were black was virtually nil.

We escaped from the Foundry and the Spring Smithy was just across the way. "Here we are, aw'll tek thi up to th' Foreman's Office an' leave thi to it."

"Harold, aw've browt thi another slave," he said, turning round to give me a wink. "He seems a bright lad, unlike some o' th'keaw-yeds they send yo."

Harold Jepson was the day-shift foreman. He wore the standard foreman's blue smock and had a pencil in his top pocket. I'd guess he was about 60 but looked nearer 80, worn down by fags and beer and the caustic atmosphere of the Spring Smithy.

"Reet, thanks Fred. Neaw then. 'David Horrocks...cat 1 shopman.' Well then David, aw'll gi thi a little tour round the shop and show you what goes on, an' then we'll get you kitted out and get thi started."

"This is where owd wagon springs are stripped apart. Hasta seen a wagon spring? It's several leaves, or plates, on top of each other which bend under th'weight of a wagon or carriage. Same as they used to have in th'days of horse-drawn carriages, nowt changes. We strip aw th'leaves apart an' then they go into that furnace, ovver theer. They come out red hot. Tha mun watch thiself; we use these tongs to grip the leaf when it comes eawt. Then they get dipped into that oil bath – on them jigs – an' they come eawt good as new. They get put back together and we send 'em off to th'Wagon Shop for re-assembly."

A lot of the blokes wore just a t-shirt and a pair of boxer shorts, apart from a leather brat to give some basic protection. Most were engrossed in the job though a couple gave me a cheery nod.

It looked easy enough. Misleading. The blokes on the jigs had the technique down to a fine art. When they lifted the hot piece of metal out of the jig they gripped it with the tongs dead in the middle. You'd need a mix of strength, dexterity and good judgement. The trick was to grip the hot metal dead centre before lifting it. If you were a fraction of an inch out it would swivel round and catch you.

The tour of the Smithy ended up back in the foreman's office and I was given my one item of protective clothing: a smith's apron – or 'brat' as they called it in the Smithy. It was no namby-pamby floral pinny but a well-used leather apron, encrusted with oil and dirt. I loved the feel and smell of it.

"Reet let's get thi started," said Harold Jepson. I was given the job of stacking the finished spring-leaves. It seemed easy enough at first but after a few dozen I started to ache. And there was no let up. The Smithy operated a bonus system which depended on everyone pulling their weight and if you couldn't keep up you'd be unpopular, to put it mildly. No wonder so many asked for their cards by Friday. By dinner-time I was aching all over.

I was shown where to make a brew and I'd brought some cheese sandwiches. I was joined by a couple of the lads off the jigs, Barry and Ged, a bit older than me but not much, mid-20s I'd guess.

"Everyone aches like fuck th' first couple of days," said Ged. "You'll get used to it. It's better than th'Foundry."

"If they put you on th'jigs," my other new workmate, Barry, added, "for fuck's sake be careful. If the metal swivels round and catches you, it's fucking agony. It's never happened to me – yet – but I've seen it with some of the other blokes. Sometimes their arm would be half off, with the iron biting into the flesh like a hot knife going through butter. Smelt like a barbecue. They'd whisk 'em off to the medic straight away before the ambulance arrived, and you'd not see them for a few months. Some never came back, an' I can't blame 'em."

We clocked off at 4.30, I'd never felt time move so slowly. And I was knackered.

"Dosta think tha'll stick it then?" asked foreman Harold as I hung my brat up in the mess area.

"Oh aye, I'll be fine when I get used to it," I replied, wanting to lie down and die.

What a relief it was coming out of the door and into the fresh air. It was early summer but it must have been 15 degrees cooler outside. I'd left my bike parked up by the gatehouse and I felt every inch of that Golden Mile. I got home at 5 and went straight to bed.

Except I couldn't sleep.

This is bloody stupid, what am I doing? I could get myself a boring nine-to-five job in Bolton town hall. Wouldn't be demanding but I wouldn't be coming home feeling that I wanted to lie down and die.

I'm very good at saying 'that's it, I've had enough'. All I needed to do was ring in tomorrow morning and tell Personnel I'd found something else, thanks for taking me on, goodbye. They probably expected it.

Something kept telling me to stick it out.

The alarm clock sounded at 6.30 and I arrived just after 7, coming in at the south gatehouse, closer to the Smithy. I left my bike in the shelter and walked down, meeting foreman Harold who was just in front of me.

He looked surprised to see me. "Thowt you'd had enough lad," Harold said, stubbing his fag out on the bench. "They reckon that if you can get thi first couple o'days over wi' tha'll manage."

Barry was already in the locker room, putting on his 'brat'. "Aw reet Dave, we're early, let's geet a brew on."

He was from Wigan – his accent totally different from the local speech – and a keen Rugby League player. He'd been signed for the Wigan junior team but couldn't put the time in between work and girlfriends.

There was a serious side to him as well. Over our dinner break we got talking about novels – I'd seen a well-thumbed copy of Tess Of The D'Urbervilles lying among a pile of union magazines and Playboys by his locker. It turned out he was a keen reader and we got into conversation about favourite novelists. He loved the classics – Dickens, Hardy and a special liking for Arnold Bennett.

"I like the way he writes about th'Potteries. A bit like here in a way. He understands life, unlike that twat George Orwell who knew fuck all abeawt Wigan."

That seemed a bit unfair. I was a huge fan of Orwell and Homage to Catalonia was one of my favourites. "Aye, he were a socialist o' sorts but deep down a middle class southern toff as looked down on th'likes of us, Dave."

I hadn't expected to be involved in a debate on English literature on the second day of my career at the Loco. But that was typical; you never knew what lay beneath these foul-mouthed but fundamentally decent blokes. That half-hour lunch break on Tuesday morning was the beginning of my real education.

It was a different world to university. The only feminine presence was a few cheesy pictures pinned up around the mess area – tits and arses, usual sort of stuff, lifted out of soft porn mags like the ones Barry kept alongside Thomas Hardy. Some of the shop stewards tried to remove them but they soon went back up. It wasn't that big a deal, at least back then.

I don't ever remember seeing a woman in the shop all the time I was there. That'd be about five years – when they announced they were shutting us down. A couple of women journalists stuck their heads through the door during the closure campaign but they weren't allowed in, on 'safety grounds'. We had to work in the place all the time, safe or not.

After a few weeks I'd had enough of stacking wagon springs and was relieved when Harold came along and asked if I fancied doing 'a bit o' strikin''. This seemed an odd request but it wasn't about mounting a picket line, rather about working as a blacksmith's assistant. The smith would hold the hot metal by a small pair of tongs and his 'striker' would hit it with a big hammer. Again, it was more difficult than it looked and I was put to work with Sam Baines, a miserable ill-tempered old bugger at the best of times.

"Hit the bloody thing square on lad," he implored. After missing a couple of times, nearly hitting him instead of the metal, he threw his hands up in disgust.

"Tha's not med out for this lad."

But I was in luck. There was a vacancy on the jigs after one of the lads had got a nasty burn and was off sick. I'd be working with Barry and Ged so I was up for it. My attempts at using the tongs were more successful than my short time as a blacksmith's striker. I got the hang of catching the hot metal dead centre and lifting it out of the jig. We could have a laugh and the time went pretty quickly.

Like lots of places that were hell to work in, there was a sort of camaraderie in the Spring Smithy. I soon got to know the other blokes doing different jobs around the shop, as well as Barry and Ged. We'd look out for each other and share our snap if some of the men's wives were more generous with the sandwiches. If someone dropped a bollock that might have got him in trouble, we'd do our best to cover.

And the foremen were mostly OK. As long as the job got done and the bonus targets were met, they were happy. And so were we. That's why we took risks and cut corners so we'd get finished earlier, while the poor bastards in the Foundry had to work right up to the clock.

It was bloody hard work at The Loco, whether you were in The Smithy or Mech. Foundry. But after a few weeks I began to feel on top of it. My legs and arms stopped aching. I could go to bed at a normal time after a few pints and wake up without feeling like shit.

After six months I was told to report to Personnel to collect my travel pass. 'D. Horrocks, Privilege Card, British Railways Board, BREL Horwich'. It was to open up a new world for me. I'd get so many free passes a year to travel wherever I wanted.

"Make sure you don't lose it," the chap in the office said as he handed over the blue bit of card. "And if you get caught lending it out to any of your mates, you'll be getting a different sort of card."

I felt like I was a part of this bloody place. I'd stuck it out. Nobody was more surprised than I was.

Dry Run: Alberta goes to Blackpool

Driver and fireman pose for the camera on the footplate of 45562 "Alberta" whilst awaiting the `right-away' from Blackpool Central.

"Get th'bag in Jim," his driver shouted across the footplate as they pulled into Huddersfield station at the head of a Friday night 'illuminations special' to Blackpool.

"Let's mek sure we get a run through beawt stoppin' anywher else. There'll be a pint waitin' for us in th' railway club."

Jim Holt climbed up onto the tender and his mate 'turned on the tap' – a large wheel which released a torrent of water into the engine's tender. A few minutes later it started to overflow, flooding the top of the tender and soaking Jim's feet as well.

"Stop paddlin' and get back on, we're gooin'!" shouted his mate. "We've a passenger toneet but tha'll be stood up most o'th'road."

The guard's whistle echoed down the platform. Joe Singleton, 35 years at Bolton, ten as a 'booked' driver, nodded in acknowledgment and gradually eased the locomotive's regulator open. Within seconds the engine moved forward, Joe pulling back the reversing gear steadily. They were away and their engine sure-footedly lurched into Huddersfield Tunnel, dragging its 10 coaches filled with West Riding millworkers and their families off to the see 'the lights' for the weekend.

It was an unusual job. Bolton men had been rostered to work the 'Fridays only' special from Leeds to Blackpool because Farnley (Leeds) men couldn't get home within their day. Not many

Bolton men had route knowledge over Standedge but Joe's route card was extensive, or at least so he claimed. Joe and his mate had travelled to Leeds 'on the cushions' and relieved the Farnley crew as they arrived into Platform 12 with the empty stock from Neville Hill. The crowd of weekend trippers waiting on the platform was large and good-natured, quite a few them already well oiled.

The locomotive was an LMS 'Jubilee' – or just a '5X' to locomen – number 45562, 'Alberta'.

"She's not a bad 'un," the Leeds driver said as he climbed out of the cab. "But heavy on coal. You're mate'll be sweeping th' tender by th'time you get to Blackpool."

"Aye, we'st be goin' for a pint or two when we get theer and we'll not be hangin' about on th'way. We'st be catchin' th'pigeons."

Blackpool was another country, a different place far removed from the looms and spinning frames of Batley, Dewsbury and Mirfield, where they picked up more excursionists. The 'West Riding Illuminations Special' was a clever piece of British Railways marketing: a cheap weekend, with train fare and board all-in for just over £3. Not bad marketing for the '60s.

Tonight, Joe and his mate had a guest riding with them – Steve Howcroft, 18 years old and an avid steam enthusiast. He'd managed to fix up a ride on the footplate through a friend of his, Dave Hurst, another 'enthusiast' and a passed cleaner at the shed. Word had got back that the ride was 'on' but to join at Huddersfield, away from the eyes of any 'black macs' in Leeds who might object.

Steve shouted up to the driver while his mate had the 'bag' in the tender, introducing himself.

"Aye, lad, come up, Dave Hurst towd us you were joining us. Hope you don't mind getting mucked up – and tha'll be expected to work thi passage!"

While the passengers sat back and opened their own bottles of beer, the fireman of 'Alberta', one of the last remaining 'Jubilees' at Farnley Junction, settled down to an eight-mile gruelling climb up into the Pennines. It was mid-October 1966 and steam in Yorkshire had just over a year before it was all over.

"Get some rock on Jimmy lad," Joe yelled above the roar of the exhaust, bouncing back off the tunnel roof into the cab. "We'st need all th' help we can get with this owd girl."

Jim Holt slammed the shovel into the bottom of the tender, filling it with best Yorkshire steam coal, swivelling back to face the fire-hole and smoothly letting the shovel hit the bottom lip of the fire-hole. The coal was propelled into the firebox as Jim's face was lit up by the bright red glare of the fire. It looked so easy.

"Tha can sit down now cock," Joe motioned towards the young lad huddled by the tender. "That twat of an inspector can't see us now."

"He can do a bit of firing if he likes" shouted Jim.

"Leave the lad alone – he doesn't want fert get his hands chafed."

They smiled at each other. Joe, 40 years on the footplate, Jim 25 years. Jim had been regular fireman for Singleton some five years now, and they were like older and younger brothers, with repartee to match.

Steve Howcroft sat on the hard wooden fireman's seat, just in time to see the front end of 'Alberta' emerge into the dusk of a Pennine evening. The reflection of a bright green signal light shone along the boiler, and the sound of 'Alberta' getting into her stride on the long climb up to Standedge made the hairs on his neck bristle. Beyond the terraced houses and weaving sheds of Golcar and Slaithwaite loomed the moors – Pule Hill, West Nab, Butterley, Marsden, then after that Standedge Tunnel and a long descent into Lancashire and the plains.

Jim closed the firehole door and within seconds the boiler pressure hit the red line, releasing a plume of steam from the top of the firebox. A full head of steam, engine being driven hard, but well managed. Injectors on, feed water into the boiler, just take the kettle off the boil a bit.

Steve, just past his 18th birthday, would be starting at university in a couple of weeks. His choice hadn't found much favour at his school – Sociology wasn't quite the thing for a bright young Catholic lad to be doing.

"You'll be needing to keep clear of all those atheists and communists," Father O'Riley had warned. But his mum and dad were proud enough – he could be doing Sorcery for all they were bothered. It was 'going to university' that mattered, and the residents of Cawdor Street, Farnworth, agreed that young Steve had done well for himself.

The A Level results, Steve's parents were informed, had been excellent. Steve could have his pick of Oxford or Cambridge, the head told a beaming Mr and Mrs Howcroft. But he wasn't having it. "Sorry dad – they can stuff their Oxford and Cambridge, they're not my sort of place."

"You mean there's no bloody steam engines left round there," his dad retorted. He had a point. Fred Howcroft, fitter at Bee Hive Mill, wanted the best for his son and Oxbridge would have added even more kudos in the Spinning Room – which was where Mrs Howcroft – Jean – did her 'housewives shift' in the evening.

"The lad'll decide for himself Fred – you'll not change his mind," she'd argued. So it was going to be Sociology, at Manchester. Not far from home, but he'd be going into halls for his First Year.

'Alberta' was now five miles out of Huddersfield, climbing steadily, and noisily, at about 35 mph.

"Can I have a go Jim?" asked Steve. The fireman, face red with the heat and sweat dripping down from beneath the white hankie tied round his head, didn't need asking twice.

"Thanks lad – keep it going – all round the firebox."

The apparent ease of Jim's firing was the result of ten years as cleaner, passed cleaner, then fireman at Bolton loco shed. Steve knew this, and was aware he'd look wooden and slow in comparison. A full shovel of coal was heavy, and getting the coal spread across the firebox without causing 'air holes' was difficult for a novice. A couple of lumps rolled off the shovel before Steve swung the shovel round and the coal spewed into the fire.

"Fire's over theer, not on th' bloody floor," laughed Jim. "I hope you'll sweep up after!"

"Leave the lad alone" Joe Singleton shouted across the cab, "he's giving you a breather. Do us all a favour and get them mugs o' tea poured out!"

While the fireman prepared three cups of highly-sweetened tea, Joe eased back the cut-off and the engine gathered speed as the gradient eased. Approaching the 3-mile long tunnel, speed was further reduced as the train took the sharp curve into the backbone of the Pennine hills. Standedge. The climb was over, but the work wasn't done.

"Sit thiself down now cock an' have a rest," Jim urged. "Tha's done all reet."

The line through the tunnel was level, and straight. Half-way through were water troughs, where engines could pick up water as the train moved – the faster the better. Timing had to be split second – pass the marker, wind the scoop down. Next marker, scoop up. Too quick and you lost precious hundreds of gallons. Too slow and you risked wrecking the loco's scoop.

"NOW!" Joe yelled across the cab and Jim spun the scoop handle round. They were doing maybe 50 but it seemed like 100 – roaring noise from the exhaust, the rocking and rattling of the engine, and the rushed sound of water shooting into the tender. Seconds later water started dripping down the tender backplate and Jim looked steadily towards his driver, hand at the ready to lift the scoop.

LMS Jubilee 45562 "Alberta" arrives at Huddersfield on the Leeds portion of the Leeds/Bradford–Poole train, September 1966.

"NOW!" Jim spun the handle back, getting the maximum possible benefit of the troughs. The water gauge had moved up towards full.

"That'll keep us going to Blackpool" said Jim. The train shot out of the western end of the tunnel at 60, roaring past Diggle Junction box and a friendly wave from the signalman.

"Five minutes early! If we get a good road we'll be in Blackpool in time for a pint and get the last passenger home to Bowton," Jim yelled across to his mate. "An' I'm bloody well deein' for it."

"Are you buyin' then? It'd mek a nice bloody change."

'Alberta' sped over Saddleworth Viaduct and Steve looked out across Upper Mill, with its small weaving sheds and proud stone terraces alongside, dominated by the fading outline of the Pennines and Dove Stones. Different from Bolton, with its monstrous 8-storey spinning mills and row after row of dismal red-brick terraces.

Joe Singleton moved the cut-off into 'drift', and Jim cracked open the dampers to keep the fire drawing. He shut the regulator for the first time since leaving Huddersfield. The speedo touched 70 as the train, in darkness, cut through Greenfield, round the curve at Mossley, into, out of, Scout Tunnel and slowed for Stalybridge.

An unidentified Jubilee is in familiar territory as it passes through the industrial landscape.

"He's all off for us" Jim shouted from across the cab. The train was booked non-stop to its destination, and the 'bobby' at Stalybridge had given them a clear road. A short climb up to Ashton and then another long drop into Manchester.

"It's our bloody neet t'neet," said Joe, as they ran under a string of 'greens' all the way through Miles Platting, down the bank, fast line through Victoria and then out past Threlfall's Brewery and Deal Street box.

"Never mind gazing at the brewery, lad, work to be done!" Joe shoved the regulator into half-open and the three-cylinder beat echoed across the city: Manchester Cathedral, Exchange station, the new Granada Studios, gaunt warehouses – mostly derelict. Ewan McColl's 'Dirty Old Town' with 'Alberta' playing its part, setting the night on fire.

The crew of this LMS Jubilee will be relieved to leave behind the confined smoky conditions as they burst out of the tunnel into sunlight.

Steam was on its last legs, and within months would be just a memory at Farnley Junction, Bolton and other places like them. Driving would be a collar and tie job, and firing – well, you'd just sit there and read the paper, if you had a job at all. But for now steam was very much alive, and late evening commuters waiting along Platform 12 for their Southport or Blackpool train home looked up from their papers at the spectacle of 'Alberta' approaching in full cry.

Steve sat in Jim's seat and watched the red hot cinders flying out of the engine's chimney. People wondered why he had this fascination for 'steam trains', why he spent so much time with his mates at the shed, when they could be out with girls, or getting drunk. As 'Alberta' pounded by Agecroft Junction, cinders flying and the engine's exhaust becoming one continuous roar as speed increased above 50, the answer to Steve seemed pretty obvious: this was the ultimate experience, and before long it would be gone. Get it now, while it was there. Now, before it's gone.

More time was gained on the gentle climb to Bolton, and much whistling was done as driver and fireman passed their home shed. Jack Beevor, running shed foreman, looked out of the office at the passing commotion and shook his head in disbelief.

"That lot again – why don't they bloody well grow up," he said laconically to his clerk, Eric Shaw. "Aye, fuckin' piss-artists," Eric replied, with a sly smile towards the passing train.

The train sailed through Bolton station and Joe prepared to accelerate towards Preston. But for the first time signals were at caution: a bright yellow light shone in the distance, telling them Dean Clough wasn't ready for them. The distant was 'on' and the home signal was at danger.

"That'll be your pal campin' on th'phone" said Jim as his mate slowly applied the vacuum brake.

Steve's 'pal' was Graham Southworth – train-booker at Dean Clough. Graham left school at the first chance and got a job with the railways. His eyesight meant he couldn't go on the footplate, but he was offered the job of train-booker for the wages of 12/6 a week. Graham's job involved recording the movement of trains in the train register book, as well as taking phone messages, and occasionally – increasingly – signalling the trains while the signalman put his feet up. Tonight he was on with Maurice Shackleton, one of Bolton's most conscientious signalmen.

As the train crawled up towards the 'home' signal, a figure could be seen moving across inside the box, tapping out a message on the block instruments, and then wrenching a signal lever. Whatever was in front – probably a stopper – had cleared. The home signal went up, and Joe eased off the brake, opened the regulator.

"Hey, you dozy pillock!" the fireman shouted up to the box, as 'Alberta' heaved its 10 coaches forward. Maurice looked out of the window with a condescending grimace, while Graham leant out of the box window to wave to Steve.

"You've a Wigan train in front, soon be out of your way. See you tomorrow night at the club?"

"Yeah – you're on!" Steve yelled back, as Alberta headed away, past Heaton's Mill, lights blazing away on every floor as the evening shift 'got agate'.

Jim got his shovel ready to start heaving more coal into Alberta's firebox, and turned momentarily to look at the mill across the sleazy Middlebrook flowing down towards the Irwell. His own parents worked long hours, all their lives, in one of those places. Both going near-deaf through the noise. The worst of it was being penned-up, start at 6, clock off at 6, day in, day out – like these poor fuckers on here, off to Blackpool for a dirty weekend. Then back on Monday to it all again. No thanks. Jim might be out of a job in a few months when they get rid of steam, but there'd be other work on the railways; there would always be something.

"What's up wi' thee? Dreamin'?" Joe rasped. "Do you want that pint or not – cos if you do, get some rock on and we'll see what this owd Yorkshire lass can do."

The line down through Chorley to Preston was easy going and high speeds could be reached if you were routed 'fast line' from Euxton. Once through the junction you were on the main line, and if you got a clear road you could really run.

Approaching the junction, on a tight right-hand curve, Jim craned his neck for the signal. "You're right away Joe! Fast Line!"

A buzz of excitement, inaudible but real, shot across the footplate. Jim shovelled a quick round of coal into the firebox, shut the firehole door and 'Alberta' soon started blowing off – full head of steam. Full regulator, cut-off at 35%. Speedo reading 50....60....75......

The train stormed through Leyland at 75, the ten coaches swaying behind; passengers waiting for a stopping train jumping clear.

Driver Peter Kirk on the footplate of a 'Jubilee' loco at Wigan North Western on a special working in June 2022

They'd reached 80 by Farington Junction when Joe shut the regulator and began applying the brakes as Preston approached, over the Ribble. Once through the station and past the junction where the main line to Scotland diverged, Joe opened the regulator wide once more and sparks lit up the Maudland sky. The loco's three-cylinder beat ricocheted off the cutting walls and a few faces peeped out from the upstairs windows of terraced houses that paralleled the railway.

They slowed for Kirkham and then followed a final burst of acceleration towards Poulton-le-Fylde. From Carleton Crossing, signals were at caution all the way into Blackpool. They'd caught up with a slower-moving diesel train.

Blackpool Tower, magnificently illuminated, drew them like a lighthouse in the darkness. They drew into Platform 6 twenty minutes early.

"Not bad for an owd un, eh?" Joe beamed across to Jim, his hand caressing the vacuum brake handle.

"Who? Thee or th' bloody engine?" asked Jim. "And you'd be buggered if it weren't for me! Are we goin' for that pint then, or what? I'm deein' for a pint o'Thwaites in th' railway club."

Joe eased his engine to a gentle stand at the stop block. Looking out of the cab he could see Harry Taylor, the duty station foreman, with a grin on his face.

"Howdo Joe!" he shouted above the sound of hissing steam. "Some bad news for you – Control have been on and they want you to work this empty stock on 5 back to Bolton. Relief on arrival. Get a brew an' then bugger off quick, we need the platform for another special."

Joe and Jim looked up along Platform 5 and could see the shape of an old 'Crab' with steam leaking from everywhere that it could.

The expression on the driver and fireman's faces was not that of unalloyed joy.

"So much for that pint then," sighed Joe. He turned to Steve who was the only one looking happy. "Anyway, lad, you've got yourself a ride home an' tha con do th' firin'."

On Golden Wings to Wakefield

Preserved Lancashire and Yorkshire 'A' Class 52322 piloted by L&Y Saddle Tank 51456, crossing Brooksbottom Viaduct, Summerseat, on the East Lancashire Railway in March 2022.

Ben Heaton was booked on at 4 a.m. He was out of the house and on his bike at 3.45. The loco sheds at Crescent Road were an easy two miles, mostly downhill. Dad was a driver at Bolton shed; aristocrats of the railway, or so they liked to think of themselves. Mum worked in the Card Room at the new Holden's mill on Blackburn Road. It was May 1911.

Ben was met by Joe Coyle, the shed time-keeper. It wasn't good news. "Mornin' Ben. Tha's geet an A Class this mornin'. Loco 1310. Regular engine's bin pinched for another job. Tha'll have fert manage."

Ben's job was to take a full train of empty wagons from Halliwell Sidings to Crofton, near Wakefield, with his regular driver Tom Brotherton. Easy enough job with a small loco like an 'A' class if they weren't over-loaded. Coming back would be a different proposition. Normally it was 50 wagons of loaded coal from the Yorkshire pits for Lancashire's mills. The job was booked for a big eight-wheeled freight engine – a 'Sea Pig' as locomen called them. They'd pull anything.

An 'A' class could only manage half of what a Sea Pig could take up the gradients coming back from Yorkshire. All steam locos are different, even members of the same class which were built to the same specification. And this one, 1310, was a notorious 'bad 'un'. Often 'shy' of steam and not as powerful as most of her classmates.

"Aw suppose we'll have fert mek a do. Hast spoke to mi driver?"

"Aye, Tom's havin' a look at her neaw. He's noan so happy noather."

When Ben got to number 9 road he could see Tom Brotherton oiling round the engine. He'd been firing for Tom for over 12 months and it had grown into a father-son relationship. Tom was in his 50s and had started on 'The Lanky' when he was 10, as a cleaner. He'd been 'booked' a driver for 10 years and was one of the shed's most respected drivers. He was well-known for his fine tenor voice – he sang in his church choir and these last two Christmases had taken lead roles in 'Messiah'. This morning, piety was notably absent.

"A right shower o'shit they've gi'n us Ben. This bugger's famous for bein' a poor steamer. Weak too. Won't pull th'skin off a rice pudding'. Aw hope tha's not on a promise wi'that lass o'thine?"

"We're supposed to be meeting this afternoon at the socialist demonstration, aw said aw'd be there for 1.00."

Ben had been 'courting' Sarah for six months now. They'd met at the Independent Labour Party meeting in Bolton on a Sunday night and had been walking out ever since, or as often as not, pedalling out with the left-wing Clarion Cycling Club.

"Tha'll be bloody lucky lad, but between us let's do eawr best. Th'revolution meyt have fert start beawt thi. An' aw were lookin' forward to a pint or two in th'Church after we'd signed off."

At 4.45 they were ready to go. 'Tender first' to Halliwell where they'd pick up their train and head back through Bolton and eastwards into Yorkshire. Tom eased open the locomotive's regulator and slowly moved out of the shed, into daylight. They'd got a full tender of coal and a tank of water.

At the top of the shed yard Ben jumped down to tell the signalman at Burnden Junction they were 'light engine to Halliwell'.

Within seconds the signal came off and they steamed past the box, to a friendly wave from Ted Blackburn, one of the regular 'bobbies'.

"What've they given you today then?" Ted shouted from the veranda. "Tha'll be lucky to get as far as Rochdale wi'that owd crock!"

"Aye, thanks Ted, thee get back to thi nice warm stove and read your bloody newspaper."

The engine trundled through the recently rebuilt Trinity Street station with its elegant long platforms. The engine stopped for a moment by the Guard's Messroom, to pick up Sam Hopkinson, one of Bolton's most experienced goods guards and noted for his foul temper and language to go with it.

"What the fuckin' 'ell's this they've given us? A fuckin' A Class? Aw just hope Control know fert reduce th' load comin' back from Crofton."

"Aye, but it's not thee as'll be shovellin' th' rock Sam," Ben said as his mate climbed onto the footplate.

"Thank Christ for that, aw durnt envy yo'."

They branched off at the far end of the station – Bolton West Junction – towards Blackburn through the short tunnel under Bradshawgate. Approaching the junction for Halliwell Sidings they slowed down to wait for the 'bobby' – Joe Croston – to pull off the signal for the branch line. The engine slowly eased round the curve onto the branch and stopped by the Yard Foreman's cabin. Joe Nelson came out to see them.

"Tha's geet forty empties – 25 for Crofton but detach 15 at Sowerby Bridge. Report to th'Yard Master at Crofton for your return working. And good luck!"

"Aye we'll need it," said Tom. "Joe, sithee, get on to Control and make sure we get a banker at Bury. We'll struggle gettin' up Broadfield with this bugger."

The engine backed down onto the train of empty coal wagons – about 400 tons behind the nder. Normally an easy job for a large freight loco but a big job for the modest six-wheel A Class. Sam walked back to his van and gave a green flag to the driver. A short toot on the whistle and ne train juddered into motion. Joe had already pulled off his signals to get the train out onto the main line' back down to Bolton. The first challenge was Bradshawgate Tunnel 'dip'. The line ropped down from the junction and over the River Croal at a steep gradient, then half way nrough the tunnel the line started climbing again up to the station. With 40 loose-coupled wagons was a challenge to a driver's expertise to keep the couplings 'taught'. If they bunched up in ne dip you'd get a nasty snatch which would throw the guard across his van and risk breaking ouplings. The guard had to keep his brake screwed down hard to assist the driver.
"Here we go then," Tom shouted across to his fireman. "Howd on. An' aw hope Sam's doin' too!"

Tom's technique was to go fairly slowly over the Croal Viaduct then open up the engine and harge through the tunnel keeping all the wagon couplings nicely taught. An added touch was to urst into one of his favourite Verdi choruses to add a touch of drama to the occasion, not that it was required. On this occasion, he decided that 'The Chorus of the Hebrew Slaves' was appropriate.

"Va', pensiero, sull'ali dorate;
Va, ti posa sui clivi, sui colli,
ove olezzano tepide e molli
l'aure dolci del suolo natal!
Del Giordano le rive saluta,
di Sionne le torri atterrate…
Oh mia Patria sì bella e perduta!"
(Go, thoughts, on golden wings;
Go, settle upon the slopes and hills,
where warm and soft and fragrant are
the breezes of our sweet native land!
Greet the banks of the Jordan,
the towers of Zion …
Oh my country so beautiful and lost!)

Perhaps stirred by Tom's rendition, that norning the signalmen at West were on the ball and made sure the train had a clear run through the station. Tom had the engine working close

A small-boilered L&Y 0-8-0 goods engine, probably near Middleton Junction, c 1900. Photo courtesy of the Lancashire and Yorkshire Railway Society.

to full power, with the cut-off extended to the maximum 75% and the regulator thrown right across. So far so good. Loco 1310 responded well and was steaming nicely as Ben shovelled more coal into the firebox. At Bolton East Tom slowed down to take the junction onto the Bury and Rochdale line, looking back as they negotiated the tight curve to make sure they hadn't had a break-away. The wagons were all intact and he was able to give a wave to Sam, who was leaning out from his brake van veranda.

They crossed Burnden Viaduct after passing Rose Hill Junction and the Wanderers' new ground. Then Darcy Lever Viaduct, looking down to the mills below, which were just starting to get into action at 6.00 a.m. Approaching Bury there's another 'dip', even worse than that at Bradshawgate – 'Bury Hollow' as locomen called it.

This time, Tom wasn't so lucky with the signals. Approaching Bury the distant signal was 'on' meaning he might have to stop at the next signal, before the dip. As the train crept up to the 'home' signal it came off and Tom opened the regulator to do his customary charge, only to find the next signal was against him. He managed to control the train without too big a 'snatch' that would have knocked Sam around in his van. At the next signalbox – Bury East – the signalman was standing outside his box.

"What're yo' playin' at bobby?" Tom yelled. "We need t' get a good road with this, not stoppin' at every bloody signal."

"Calm down owd lad, aw'm stoppin' thi because you asked for a banker, and tha's gerrin' one. Draw forward and he'll come up behind thi. Aw reet?"

"Aye, aw reet." Tom grudgingly replied. "Aw suppose aw'd better say 'thank you'."

After a few minutes they saw another A Class nudge onto the back of their train, ready to push them up the steeply-graded line through Broadfield towards Heywood. The driver of the banking loco whistled, Tom replied, and off they went.

It was still hard work going up the 1 in 82 climb past Heap Bridge Junction and Broadfield but they made it; the assisting engine dropped back after Broadfield to leave Tom, Ben and Sam to continue their way forward alone. At that time of day traffic was light and they 'got a run' at Castleton East Junction, where they joined the main Manchester–Bradford line. From the west side of the Pennines the gradients aren't as severe as coming from the east, so 1310 was able to shift the 40 wagons fairly comfortably, though not without some collar work by Ben.

Beyond Rochdale were Clegg Hall water troughs and Ben got ready to drop 'the scoop' to pick up water as the engine passed over the troughs. The amount a slow-moving train could pick up was limited but, in most drivers' view, every bit helps.

The landscape between Bolton, Bury and Rochdale was heavily industrialised punctuated by short stretches of open fields which hadn't yet succumbed to development. From Heywood it was hard to see any sign of greenery, with mills and weaving sheds clustered along the lineside, many with their own sidings to take in coal to power the boilers and transport the finished cloth or yarn. The scenery began to open up by Clegg Hall, a famous old house reputed to have its own resident ghost – or 'boggart'. The Pennine hills were getting closer, with Knowl Hill rising up above Littleborough on the left.

"We'll tek water at Sowerby Bridge," said Tom to his fireman. The line is still climbing as it enters Summit Tunnel and the exposed footplate was shrouded in smoke and steam as 1310 settled down to about 25 mph, with steam pressure starting to drop.

"We'll soon be over th'top, don't worry," Tom shouted across to Ben. "Downhill aw th'road then."

"It's not that aw'm worried about," yelled Ben above the racket. "It's comin' back!"

"Aye lad. But let's not meet trouble hauf way shall we?"

Tom eased off the regulator just over half way through the tunnel and the train drifted out the other side, through Walsden, Todmorden and Eastwood. It was a different landscape – of three-storey stone terraces, a narrow valley with the River Calder hugging the land and the Rochdale Canal vying for space. The mills were smaller than the huge cotton spinning factories of Bolton, Bury and Rochdale. There was more weaving out this way, around Walsden, Todmorden and Hebden Bridge. Cotton was gradually displaced by wool as they moved east.

"By gum we're in Yorkshire neaw!" Tom shouted across. "We'st be mashin' a brew before long...I think it calls for a song..."

Tom broke into 'The Anvil Chorus' from Verdi's Il Trovatore, one of his favourites. He'd seen it performed in Manchester last year and dreamt of hearing Caruso sing it at La Scala.

*"Vedi! Le fosche notturne spoglie
De' cieli sveste l'immensa volta;
Sembra una vedova che alfin si toglie
i bruni panni ond'era involta.
All'opra! all'opra!
Dàgli, martella."
(See how the clouds melt away
from the face of the sky when the sun shines, its brightness beaming;
just as a widow, discarding her black robes,
shows all her beauty in brilliance gleaming.
So, to work now!
Lift up your hammers!)*

After Ben sat down, the hard firing work done for now, he offered a polite round of applause.

"Tha wants fert get in that Clarion Choir, ne'er mind this cyclin' stuff,"

"Maybe one o'those days but my voice isn't owt fert write whum abeawt."

"That's what they all say," Tom answered. "Tha should give it a try."

After Mytholmroyd the train reached Luddendenfoot. "Neaw then," announced Tom. "Famous ailway literary shrine – wheer Branwell Bronte were station master but spent most of his time uppin' ale in th' village pub. Clever chap."

After Luddendenfoot Tom saw the distant signal against them, as he'd expected. Detaching wagons at Sowerby Bridge Yard was a complicated job involving reversing back onto the up line, hen drawing forward into sidings. At least there'd be yard staff on duty to assist, and a lighter load going forward.

The train came to a halt just west of Sowerby Bridge station, waiting for the signal to draw orward across to the up main. A minute later a sharp whistle was heard in the distance and one of the Lancashire and Yorkshire's crack expresses, the York–Liverpool, roared past towards Manchester with one of the Horwich-built 'Highflyers' at the front.

"They durnt know heaw lucky them Newton Heath men are wi' them injuns," said Tom. "While we're stuck with this."

Seconds after the express had passed, the ground signal cleared to allow the goods train to cross over and then reverse into the sidings. The yard staff did their job well, detaching the first fifteen wagons under Sam's watchful eye and getting Tom to shunt them onto another road. They stopped next to a water column and Ben jumped up onto the tender to 'put the bag in' and get the tender filled. Tom then drew forward again and set back onto the remaining 25 wagons for Crofton, before reversing onto the main line. The signalman changed the points to enable the train to access the east-bound 'down' line and they were away once again.

The loss of 15 wagons made the load more manageable, though it was mostly flat or downhill past Horbury Junction.

At Wakefield the line to the yard branches off to Calder Bridge and onto Crofton Sidings, one of the biggest yards in the West Riding, a collecting point for coal from the pits around Wakefield, Castleford and Featherstone.

The train was met at the yard entrance by a shunter who jumped into the cab to direct them to their arrival road.

"Han' yo' lads coom aw th'way fro' Bowtun wi'this little injun?" he asked in a nearly incomprehensible Wakefield dialect. "Why doesn't ta ask th'shed gaffer at Wakefield if he con gi' yo' owt better to geet whoam?"

"Aye it crossed mi mind," replied Tom. "But bi th' time we'd finish buggerin' abeawt we could be whom anyroad. But thanks owd lad."

The shunter uncoupled the 25 wagons and got back into the cab. "You're train's on number six road, 25 loaded coal for Bullfield Sidings, wherever that is. Aw hope tha does?"

"Oh we do, well enough" said Tom. "But 25 o'coal wi' this is injun's gooin t' be bloody hard wark."

"Aye, tha's reet. Onyroad goo an get thi snap for neaw. Tha's not due eawt while 9.30."

Tom, Ben and Sam left their engine at the head of the train of loaded coal and made their way to the cabin. There were a couple of Yorkshire crews there, Normanton men, mashing their tea and having a fry up.

"Bowtun men eh?" said one of the Normanton drivers to Ben while he was making his brew. "A long way from hooam wi' an A Class aren't tha?"

"Aye, we got lumbered wi' this instead of eawr usual engine. An' we're purgin' to get whom this afternoon."

"Footbaw? Didn't know th'Wanderers were playin' today."

"Neaw, it's a demonstration – an' aw'm meetin' someone."

"Oh aye, what sort of demonstration's that then? A union job?"

"Sort of – it's a socialist meeting. We've got one o'thi fellow countrymen speaking, Philip Snowden from Keighley."

"Oh we know him! A gradely lad. We've had him at our ILP meetings mony a time. He's one of us. Doesn't look up to much, but when he gets goin'…a sort of political equivalent of one of eawr 'Highflyers'."

The conversation over the tea urn continued for several minutes. The local driver turned out to be the union branch secretary at Normanton and chairman of the local ILP branch. Walter Hampson, a name that rang a bell with Ben.

"Haven't you been over to Bolton Socialist Club to speak on something?"

"Might have done, a year or two back. On the need for one union for all railwaymen, if I remember right. The idea still falls on stony ground with mony of 'em reawnd here."

Tom motioned to Ben that it was time to get back to their engine for the haul back over the Pennines. A prospect neither were looking forward to.

"Listen," Walter said to Tom and Ben as they finished their brew. "Why not fail your engine. Leakin' tubes, summat like that. I know the shed foreman down the road at Wakefield, I'll square it if any questions are asked. I'll get onto Control and make sure I speak to one of our ILP comrades who's on early shift today, and get 'em to agree a swop. We'll take your A Class back to Normanton shed and get the fitters to tek a look. You have our engine. It's a large-boilered eight-wheeler. It'll waltz away wi' 25 o'coal."

Tom and Ben exchanged glances, but needed little persuasion. As senior man, it was Tom's decision.

"Well, it had been givin' trouble comin' over Summit on th'way here. Aw think those tubes do need a proper look. Aw think it best if we failed her."

Walter was on the phone to Wakefield Control. He got straight through to Jeremy Martlew, his ILP comrade who happened to be manning the 'loco' desk that morning. "Sure Walter, tell the Bolton lads to take your engine and we'll square it with Manchester Control. We'll get our loco sent back on Monday morning's Halliwell-Crofton."

The restored 'Unity Hall', Nelson. Opened by the Independent Labour Party in 1908.

The men shook hands. "It's what brotherhood is all about," Walter said to Tom and Ben. "Lancashire and Yorkshire workers united! And you might just mek it back in time to hear Philip, an' see that lass o'thine, which aw think is the more urgent question."

The swap was done. All Walter and his mate Gordon had to do was take the 'failed' A Class number 1310 back to Normanton shed, drop the fire and sign off. Tom and Ben climbed up onto the footplate of the big 'Coal Engine' that they'd seen working into Bolton with Sowerby Bridge men, but hadn't worked one themselves.

"Just make sure she gets a good even fire," called up Walter's mate, who added "and durnt be scared o'working her hard. That's how they like it. Plenty o'welly. Full regulator and a long cut-off."

The 'arrangements' had made them a bit late leaving the yard. They got the right away from Sam just after 10.00 and Tom moved his new steed down to the signalbox that gave access onto the main line. They were away, swinging their train out onto the main line and past Wakefield loco shed, over Calder Bridge and through Kirkgate station.

"What d'you reckon then?" Tom asked his fireman. "Con yo' manage? It teks time gettin' used to a new class o'loco and she's a wide firebox."

"Aye, aw think aw'll manage," Joe replied. "Aw'm gettin' used."

It was a dream compared to the abandoned A Class. She had power in abundance and was a good steamer. Fire all round the firebox, nice and even. Regular and often. Coal the size of a man's fist. Keep at it. Watch the water level in the boiler. Look out for signals ahead.

All was well. Horbury Junction passed, then Thornhill. Box after box, branches weaving in and out. You needed to know your road along here.

Could anything go wrong? On the railway, anything could; often did. They were galloping nicely through Mytholmroyd then saw the distant signal 'on' as they approached Hebden Bridge. The home signal cleared as they got closer, but they could see the signalman standing on the veranda with a red flag. They ground to a halt.

"Tha's geet an hot box, reawnd about 15th wagon back," the signalman shouted. "Detach it in th' up refuge siding an' we'll have you on your way."

Looking back they could see smoke and some flames coming from one of the wagons. Sam was running up by the side of the train to have a look. The ageing wagon had developed a hot axlebox, all too common with some of the old coal wagons that the L&Y were still using. Sometimes it would be lack of lubrication, or slurry had got into the axlebox. Whatever the reason, if it was allowed to continue the axle could break and the wagon derail. Carrying on wasn't an option.

"Bloody hell," thought Ben. "This'll set us back half an hour." The chances of getting to Bolton for 1.00 were receding, rapidly. Ben helped Sam uncouple the wagon and Tom drew the train forward past the box. The bobby shifted the points to allow Tom to reverse the front portion of the train into the refuge siding where Sam would hook off the defective wagon. Then they'd have to move forward again, out onto the main line and reverse onto the rest of the train. Then they'd be away.

They waved goodbye to the Hebden Bridge 'bobby' at 11.15, with Tom shoving the regulator over to full as the gradient up to Summit started to bite.

"If we get a road we'll have you back for your bloody meeting in time," Tom shouted above the loud exhaust of the engine as Ben started shovelling regular rounds of coal into the firebox. The train was picking up speed as they rounded Charlestown Curve to see Eastwood's distant signal on.

"Bloody hell, what's goin' on neaw?" Tom shouted to his mate. They drew up to the signalbox and the signalman leant out of the window.

"Sorry lads, Control orders. You're running out o'course and unless we get you eawt o'th'road you'll delay th' Liverpool express. You're goin' inside the up loop. Tha's reet to draw forrud."

Bloody Control, but not much they could do about it. Tom gently opened the regulator and the train drew forward into the loop to allow the express to pass. They must have been there 15 minutes before the Liverpool express shot past with another 'Highflyer' on the front. The Newton Heath men waved to Tom as they galloped by.

A minute later the signal cleared to let the coal train out onto the main line and they were away again. It was 12.00 and the meeting on the town hall steps was just starting, Ben remembered.

"Go for it Tom, we've a tender full o'coal, th'sooner we get back to Bowtun the better."

Tom opened the regulator to full once more, extending cut-off on the valve gear to 50%. The train belched a pall of smoke over Todmorden as Ben put on more coal. The sound from the hard-working loco would have woken the dead from the nearby cemetery at Walsden, before they plunged into Winterbutlee Tunnel, and then the longer Summit bore.

From the top of the climb, in the middle of the tunnel, Tom was able to ease off steam and drift down through Littleborough and into Rochdale. They passed Castleton East at 12.35. This time they were going down Broadfield Bank instead of up it, and careful management of the train through 'Bury Hollow' had them approaching Radcliffe just before 1.00.

"Well Ben young lad, tha con have a bit o'rest neaw an' look forrud to seein' that lass o'thine."

This time Tom broke into Bizet's Carmen, singing in 'Lancashire English' this time:

Let's go, en guard! Let's goo! Let's goo! Ah!
Toreador, en guard! Toreador, Toreador!
And dream away, aye, dream in combat,
That a black eye is watching thee,
An' that love awaits thee,
Toreador, love awaits thee!
An' dream away, aye dream in combat,
That a black eye is watchin' thee
And may love await you,
Fireman, love await you!

"Heaw abeawt that then?" Tom looked across the footplate with a twinkle in his eye. Ben smiled back and looked out for the signals for Rose Hill Junction. All clear.

They drifted down towards Bolton East Junction and the signals remained clear for them to get through Bolton station. They still had to get their 25 wagons into Bullfield Sidings, hook off and get back to shed to dispose of the loco. Bullfield was less than half a mile beyond the station, on the route to Lostock. The signalman at Bullfield East was ready for them, and got them into the sidings without delay. Ben jumped down to uncouple the loco and Sam ran up to join them on the footplate.

"Light engine, shed, bobby!" Ben shouted to the signalman.

"Don't worry, we'll get thi whom," Eric Mayoh called back. "What's the big rush?"

A postcard picture of Blackburn Clarion Cycling Club members, c 1905.

They shot off through the series of tunnels before Bolton station, dropping Sam off on the platform as they slowed down to walking pace. Then Tom opened up the engine to race towards the shed. It was 1.25.

They came onto the arrival road where the engine would be coaled and then fire cleaned. That would be another 15 minutes or more. Fortunately there were no other engines on the disposal road and Harry Aldred and Joe Withers were the disposal team on duty.

"You two look like tha's done mooar than a day's work awready. Bugger off an' we'll sort out the engine. What is it? Aw've nur sin one o'these buggers befoor."

"Oh, we've kidnapped it from Yorkshire..."

When Tom and Ben signed off, they realised what Harry Aldred meant. Ben's face was black from coal dust and the rest of him was filthy as well.

"Sithee lad, tha cornt go an' see that lass o'thine lookin' like that. Aw've a change o'clothes in mi locker, meyt be a bit big for thi but they'll do..."

Within a couple of minutes Ben had washed the surface coal dust off and changed into Tom's spares. They were several times too big but they'd have to do.

Ben jumped onto his bike and pedalled off towards town, hoping to hear the sounds of the Blackburn Socialist Brass Band who'd been hired for the occasion. He caught sight of the procession coming down Deansgate, with the Clarion cyclists – and Sally looking resplendent, with her red bicycle at the front.

"Where the 'eck have you been? And what're those clothes you're wearing?" Sally laughed. "Come here an' give us a kiss, thought your engine had got lost..."

"It had, but we pinched another one."

'That Paki in the Brake Van'

Blackburn train crew driver Brian Holmes and guard Abdul Qureshi at Clitheroe, in front of the first train to use the re-opened station for 'Dalesrail' services, c 1977.

It was 1975. The London Midland Region of British Rail was recruiting to cover a number of vacancies caused by a big increase in work at Blackburn depot. Long-distance freight trains were being diverted from the West Coast Main Line via Blackburn and the Settle-Carlisle Line as electrification north of Crewe went ahead. We were being told, I'll not say by whom, that it was 'the age of the train'.

There was an advert in The Bolton Evening News for guards. I'd left school at 16 and worked for a couple of years at Warburton's bakery. My dad wanted me to join him in the mill; he worked at Swan Lane.

"Do what you like but they won't have the likes of us on the railway. Stick with your own kind."

"No thanks dad, things are changing. It's not like when you came over from Kashmir."

"Well my son, I'll let you find out for yourself."

I applied to the railway and had a perfunctory interview with someone from 'Personnel' at the Blackburn Area Manager's office. I can't say that I was greeted with open arms.

"We don't have any others like you," he said – with more than a slight edge to it. "But I suppose beggars can't be choosers."

I was told to report to Guard's Training School at Lancaster on 15th September 1975. Still got the letter somewhere. There were five other new recruits, all of us from outside the industry.

The traditional promotional ladder for a guard was, at the very least, to have worked as a porter or shunter before being elevated to the role of guard. By the 1970s those arrangements no longer applied and BR struggled to retain staff. In that disparaging term used by 'old hand' railwaymen, guards were now being recruited 'from off the street' with no prior railway knowledge. Not proper railwaymen, especially if you were black.

The course lasted about six weeks and I was taught basic railway operational principles by two venerable 'movements inspectors' who had spent a lifetime running trains. After a few days I became less conscious of standing out like a sore thumb. I was the only Asian there. No women. I became good friends with one lad, part of the same intake, Mick Grimshaw. He was an activist in one of the socialist groups, big on anti-racism, always mithering me to go on one of his demos against the National Front. No thanks Mick, I just wanted a quiet life.

We were instructed in basic railway rules, operating principles and other essentials of running trains. Although we'd be working passenger trains, none of our training concerned itself with such modern notions as 'customer service'. But I was taught how to set up a buckeye coupler, use a shunting pole and understand the essentials of brake forces.

We were given an examination in rules and regulations before being 'passed out' at the end of the eight-week course. The next stage of my induction was to 'sign on' at Blackburn depot and start 'road learning' so that I'd be able to take over as a guard as quickly as possible.

At the time, Blackburn depot was a busy place. It had absorbed displaced drivers and a few guards from Rose Grove which had closed a few years earlier, as well as Accrington which had finished in the late 1960s.

Most of the 'Blackburn men' were from Lower Darwen steam depot which had closed in 1966. This amalgam of three different depots, with their own ways of doing things, could have been a recipe for trouble. Yet everyone got on pretty well with each other. It was a totally male domain, overwhelmingly white. Apart from me, Ibrahim Qureshi. "That Paki cunt in the brake van," as one driver referred to me, thinking I couldn't hear him.

The first routes I had to learn were Preston to Colne and sidings such as Burnley goods yard, Blackburn Taylor Street and Whitebirk Colliery. We also did Blackburn to Manchester for the various passenger turns on that line, and Blackburn to Carlisle, through the heart of the Yorkshire Dales. Train spotters knew it as 'The Long Drag' but all the guys at Blackburn still called it 'The Midland', after the company that built it in the 1870s.

If the job was single-manned – meaning it didn't have a 'secondman' in the cab – most drivers were happy for me to join them in the front cab, instead of the rear of the loco, if the train was 'fully fitted' and didn't need a brakevan at the back of the train. The odd one or two told me to "get int' back cab". Racism? To be honest they were like that with the other guys I'd passed out with.

The route from Blackburn to Hellifield was hilly, lots of ups and downs. It was more difficult for a guard working that section of line than 'the Midland' itself. There were several dips where the line descended steeply and then rose with equal severity. In those situations it was easy to get a 'snatch' if you weren't careful. The wagons would bunch up and when the driver put on power to get up the oncoming gradient, the wagons would 'stretch' creating a ripple effect which would be felt – often with nasty consequences – in the guard's brake van.

A typical guard's brake van hadn't changed since the 1860s. I kid you not! There was no lighting other than what you could provide with your hand lamp, which was mainly intended to give signals to the driver and to enable you to pick your way down the side of the train. By the 1970s the old-style guard's paraffin-lit hand lamps had been replaced by powerful battery-operated 'Bardic' lamps.

On one of the first days' 'on the job' training in Blackburn yard we were taken inside a brake van. One of the other trainees innocently asked "So where's the toilet"?

The response from Joe Grimshaw, the old-hand guard who'd been rostered to show us round, was ironic. "Toilet? Tha'll be asking wheer th'fuckin' shower and bathroom is next."

A guard's brake van did at least have a stove – coal-fired of course – and a seat. That was it. No lighting, no creature comforts. So a four-hour trip to Carlisle involved either strong bowel control or taking your chance on the veranda. For major bowel movements the guard would 'do his business' inside the van on a sheet of newspaper, then hurl the parcel onto the lineside. Primitive? It certainly was. But there were compensations. To stand on the rear veranda of a goods train on a summer's day heading up to Ribblehead was sheer bliss. You were lord of all you surveyed. I never felt so close to Allah as when I was crossing that viaduct, with Ingleborough in the distance.

Blackburn guard Jack Mellor has a quick fag while leaning out of his brake van. Rose Grove, c 1977.

And another advantage of the brake van was that I could say my prayers, without interruption. I've never been especially devout but it's important to me. Needless to say, when I was at the depot there were no facilities and I didn't dare ask.

The stove, once well alight, gave off a powerful heat and you could keep your 'billy can' of tea or coffee warmed up nicely on the top of the stove. Sometimes the stoves could be difficult to get going and a supply of paraffin was always useful to get the fire blazing, with the help of newspaper and a bit of kindling.

Woe betide a guard who handed over his train and the fire was out. This once happened with me, shortly after I'd 'passed out', on a cold winter's evening working down from Hellifield to Blackburn. I was relieved by a Crewe guard, who was not happy at finding a cold van for his two hour run to Basford Hall. I could imagine him regaling his mates in the messroom, "that bloody Paki kid, couldn't even keep the fuckin' fire going."

I never encountered much really nasty stuff, to my face. What they said about me behind my back wasn't of interest. I do remember going into the staff toilets at the station to see someone had scrawled above one of the wash basins that 'Qureshi the Paki is a cunt'.

Nice. That said, some of the passengers could be worse. I was working a local up from Preston one Saturday afternoon and I recognised one of the local National Front guys, Kingston Davies, getting on the train. He'd narrowly missed getting onto the council and really thought he was somebody. And he was....

"Tickets please, sir," I politely asked as we left Preston. Most of the passengers complied. Then I reached Mr Davies.

"Why are you asking for my ticket? I've paid my fare, are you suggesting I'm a fare evader?"

"I'm the guard of the train sir, and I'm doing my job. Please show me your ticket."

I saw that this could escalate into something a bit unpleasant. A group of Blackburn Rovers fans sat behind – white lads, the worse for drink, intervened.

"Show him your fucking ticket you stupid twat," one of them shouted, to laughter up and down the train.

Sheepishly, he reached for his wallet and produced his ticket. It was a day return from Blackburn to Preston, dated from last week.

"I'm very sorry sir, but this ticket appears to be a week out of date. Are you sure you've got the correct ticket?"

More laughter from the 'Rovers' crowd.

"Hmmm...I seem to have mislaid it, perhaps you could you give me the benefit of the doubt?"

"'I'm afraid I don't have the authority to do that sir, and the barrier staff at Blackburn would expect you to show a valid ticket. I'm afraid I'll have to charge you for a single from Preston to Blackburn. That will be 58p."

By the time we'd sorted out his ticket transaction we were coming into Blackburn. He got out making loud comments about "British Rail will take any sort of riff-raff these days" to anyone who would listen.

One of the Rovers fans, who had supped at least three cans of McEwans since leaving Preston, came up to me and put his arm round my shoulder.

"You played a blinder there kid," and staggered off.

Most of the guys, when I'd shown I could do the job, were friendly and would share their brew with me when I was in the front cab. One or two had been to India and travelled on the railways.

When they asked where I was from, I had to answer 'Daubhill'.

After a few weeks I 'signed the road' for all the routes I'd been instructed to learn. My first job – 3rd February 1975 – was 'Target 17' – the Burnley 'trip' goods where we shuffled around East Lancashire with our loco 25248. It didn't go well. I developed a tooth abscess and had to leave the job for a couple of hours for an emergency appointment. It was with a very bad-tempered Irish dentist, but he did the job and I returned ready for more shunting, with a very sore mouth. The grins on the shunters' faces suggested they knew what Mr O'Rourke was like.

Which reminds me of an old racist saying that some of the guys came out with now and again, bemoaning the rapid promotion of 'them blacks' (or worse) especially down south around London. 'From head hunter to head shunter'.

I was put in the Spare Link which meant I could do any job that came along, providing I had the route knowledge. So I found myself doing a mixture of passenger trains up to Colne and back to Preston, the Manchester line, some local shunting jobs and – my favourite from the start – freights to Carlisle. One job involved signing on at 23.36 and relieving the Brewery Sidings (Manchester) to Carlisle freight at Blackburn and working it just as far as Hellifield. The run only took about an hour.

We'd usually arrive at about 01.00 and then have a five hour wait for the returning Carlisle– Brewery which we again just worked to Blackburn. Fortunately the old waiting room was converted to a train crew messroom and still had long upholstered benches. With luck, we'd get about five hours' sleep before our return working arrived.

The drivers I worked with were OK. One or two were wary about this 'Paki kid' who was a new starter but I managed to establish a rapport with most of them. Quite a few of them called me that just out of habit, not meaning any offence.

There was 'The Paki Shop' and 'Paki food', with more and more of my workmates enjoying an occasional curry. When I was in the messroom I was careful not to bring in 'spicy' food in case I'd get some comments – but a cold chapati with some paneer and a bit of chutney was fine. And the pies from the decrepit caravan outside the station were pretty good, flooded with mushy peas.

During my time as a guard, if we were at a 'foreign' depot with time to spare before the next job, we'd head to the nearest pub or railway club, where you'd join dozens of other drivers and guards doing the same thing. I stuck to orange juice, often to my mate's amusement.

Being in the Spare Link had advantages in terms of getting interesting jobs, providing you had good route knowledge. I made it my business to do a bit of freelance route learning when spare, rather than playing cards in the messroom. Some routes could be easily added, such as Blackpool and Southport, handy for seasonal specials and nice easy 'day jobs'.

My first job 'over the Midland' all the way to Carlisle was on a Friday at the end of October. I signed on at 14.00 to work the fully-fitted 6M86 St Blazey to Carlisle. It was loaded to 25 wagons, carrying china clay from the Cornish mines, 575 tonnes. It was running late so as 'spare guard' I fell for the job. The driver was former Lower Darwen man George Middleton with ex-Rose Grove secondman Tony Whittle, our loco a powerful Class 47 diesel.

They were both nice friendly guys with plenty of tales to tell and I rode in the front cab with them arriving at Kingmoor Yard at 17.45. Our return working was a part-fitted train – Carlisle– Stoke, a regular Blackburn job; a big train, with not much of a 'fitted head'. The 30 wagons equalled 45 with a weight of nearly a thousand tonnes. Our loco was one of the heavy English Electric workhorses, a Class 40. We left Carlisle as it was going dark and got as far as Kirkby

tephen when I felt the train drawing to a stop. I could see the driver and signalman talking and a
w minutes later the train drew forward to the 'advanced starter' which brought the back of the
ain – with me in the brake van – next to the box.
"Make yourself comfortable lad," the signaller shouted. "You'll be here a while yet. One in
ont's struggling and not passed Ais Gill yet. Come up and make a brew if you want."
It's always bad manners to refuse a brew on the railway and I'd never been in a signalbox before.

I was surprised to see that the 'signalman' was a woman. Whatever next? I'd heard about
iv Nelson, a relief signalman between Ais Gill and Appleby (the railway lexicon did not, then,
cognise terms such as 'signaller' or 'signalwoman'). She was famous for riding to work on a big
arley Davison which accentuated her tiny figure even more.
I think we were equally surprised to see each other. She was the first to break the ice.
"Well, we don't see many Asians up here son. How long have you been on the railway then?"
I explained I was a new starter 'from off the street' and had passed out a few months ago.
"Enjoyin' it then? I've been here thirty five years and I'm looking' forward to retirement. They
ok me on during the war – along with a few other lasses. Most of the signalmen were in the
rces and this line was operating flat out – troop trains, ammunition trains, you name it. I loved it.
I hadn't gone on the railway I'd have stayed at the farm, mucking out the stables, gettin' me arm
uck inside a sheep givin' birth and getting up at five o'clock ivvery mornin'. Doin' this I only hev
get up that time every third week."
The kettle came to the boil and she set a large mug of tea down next to me.
"What about you then lad? So, without bein' nosey, do you get much shit from the blokes you
ork with?"
"To be honest, not much. I think they see me as a bit of an oddity really. Maybe the occasional
ne but they're OK."
"Aye, I've been doin' this job longer than most of these blokes and yet they still think it's a bit
ueer havin 'a lass' – I'm old enough to be their mother, most of 'em – working in a signalbox. The
nly time I've had a bad experience was when I had a visit from one of the managers – stuck-up
ugger he was – and he tried it on a bit. I soon saw him off and that was the last I saw of him."

I was enjoying my brew when I heard a single bell ring on the block shelf. Viv jumped up and
cknowledged it, then got a rapid string of more bell signals – four rings in rapid succession, then
ne - 'is line clear for loose-coupled freight train?' She sent the signal back and got the 'line clear'
rom Ais Gill signalbox.
"Reet, he's on his way to Healey Mills, hopefully he'll not get in your way before Hellifield. Back in
our van then lad, I'll clear my starter as soon as you're in. Nice meeting you! Oh, and tek one of these..."
I'd been looking at the carcasses of several rabbits tied up outside the box, on the veranda, and
vondered what they were there for. At first I thought it might have been some kind of pagan ritual...'
"Oh, it's an old tradition among some of the signalmen. They go out shooting rabbits and tie
hem outside the box. If a train gets stopped – these things can be arranged – they'll pop in and
ake a couple back home for their wives to cook."
"So what do I owe you then? I love rabbit stew!"
"Oh, nowt. But next time you're on this job bring us a nice curry. You can't get a decent madras
ound here. I'll make sure you get stopped for a minute!"
Another job I often copped for was the 'salt train', Winsford to Carlisle, taking rock salt from the
Cheshire salt pits to Scotland. It was notorious for its habit of 'running hot' - in other words getting

a hot axlebox. The ancient wagons leaked badly and when it rained the water mixed with the salt to drip down onto the wheelsets and axleboxes. So you had to constantly be on the lookout for tell-tale signs of 'running hot'. This was usually a trail of smoke, or sometimes an actual fire.

It was fully-fitted so I was sitting in the front cab with Chris Watson, one of my favourite drivers and a talented musician who played in a small orchestra when shifts allowed. He had a great singing voice and would often burst into song – anything from Verdi to George Formby!

On this occasion he was doing his Frank Sinatra routine. When we got past Newsholme, south of Hellifield, I pulled down the cab window to look along the train to check for trouble. Sure enough, I could see smoke coming from towards the back end of the train.

"Shit, Chris. We've a hot box."

"Sinatra was always bad luck. Inside at Hellifield then, get your shunting gloves on."

We drew up outside the box at Hellifield and told the signalman to put us 'inside' while we detached the offending wagon. It was the 37th wagon of a total consist of 40, just my luck. It meant a long walk back to carry out the shunting moves.

By now it was snowing and freezing cold. I got off the loco after we'd come to a stand in one of the sidings and walked back to unhook the wagon. Replacing the vacuum hose for the brakes took longer than usual: it was frozen and my hands were numb.

My driver, Chris, thought I'd got out and given him the signal to draw forward. I hadn't. I was still in between the wagons when the train started moving. In that situation there's only one thing you can do, and that is to lie down in the 'fourfoot'. The alternative is to risk losing a leg, or two, trying to get out. It seemed to take an age for the train to pass over me, not helped by the dripping of salty water from the wagons. I was well and truly pissed on.

Eventually the train came to a stand and I walked up to the loco, still shaking, to give my mate a good bollocking. He was mortified at what he'd done. I went back down the train and uncoupled, then signalled Chris to draw forward, put the 'cripple' down another siding and then come back for the rest of the train. It only took half an hour, though it was 30 minutes I'll always remember.

We were relieved by Carlisle men who had worked south to Blea Moor with the Carlisle–Warrington. We arrived at Blea Moor at 15.05 with just 20 minutes to make a brew and admire the snowy landscape around Batty Moss and Ingleborough. The journey back, in a nicely warmed brake van, was uneventful, with time for prayers. I had a lot to thank Allah for, like still being alive!

I was enjoying life as a guard but the combination of travelling from Bolton to Blackburn, and the unsocial hours, made me think of a change. At the end of February I noticed a class 'A' supervisor vacancy at Bolton – and decided to go for it. To my surprise, I got the job. I think BR had finally realised that they had to open the door a bit wider to blacks and Asians. There were already a couple of supervisors in Manchester, Jamaican lads. I was the first Asian to get into the 'salaried' grades, even as a lowly 'class A', at least in the North-West.

My last job as a guard was, appropriately, a Carlisle turn. I was teamed with Driver Ken McIntosh on 6L46 – fully-fitted, so a 'front cab' job – and the journey went smoothly apart from being bricked as we left Blackburn. All part of a day's job. Fuckin' Asian kids too, little bastards!

My years as a guard at Blackburn were anything but uneventful and I'll never forget the men I worked with, even when they occasionally tried to kill me and a few of them called me 'that Paki cunt in the brake van'. These days I'm 'that Paki cunt who's Director of HR at Northern Trains'.

aving Horwich Loco

'anchester No. 1 branch of the National Union of Railwaymen is prominent in this view of a trade union rally in Manchester, 1977.

he announcement that the Loco Works was closing came as a bombshell. The first most of us knew about it was the headline in The Bolton Evening News for 30th June 1983. A total of 1300 workers would be redundant – an entire community would be devastated. The unions ɔt together, through the Works Committee, to form a protest campaign – 'Save Horwich Loco'.

We invited local shopkeepers, the churches, anyone who wanted to do something. Our first ɩnd-raiser was a folk night in the RMI Club, right opposite the works gate. The original name was ₹ailway Mechanics Institute', lineal descendant of the old institute long since demolished. Unlike its ɽy predecessor it had a bar and a huge concert room. The local morris dancers agreed to perform ɔr free and lots of local musicians did the same. The concert room was packed and we raised about ⸴500. We were getting there, but we needed to up our game and take the fight to 'the enemy'.

We held a special Works Committee Meeting and it was agreed that we organise a special train to ɩke us down to London to lobby Parliament – and that we invite the whole town to join us. Every ɩember of the Committee was told to start raising money for the campaign. We had a small fighting ɩnd that amounted to about £1000 including the concert money. To run the train alone we'd need early double that.

My wife, Midge, from the 'white collar' TSSA union, had volunteered to organise the special train ɔom BR. She knew a couple of blokes from her union in the divisional HQ in Manchester who made ɩre we got a cheap rate. She reported to the next meeting of the campaign committee:

"It's all sorted out. Tuesday September 12th. Leaves Chorley at 06.30, stops to pick up at ɩdlington, Blackrod and Bolton. We arrive Euston at 10.30. It's a 12 coach train and we've room for '00. We'll have a lobby of Parliament at 12.00. Bring your own food. And I've done a good deal with ɦe special trains unit, we've got it for £500."

"Well done Midge," Tommy, the works convenor, said. "But how are we going to get down to Parliament from Euston? It'll be a nightmare getting on the tube?"

"Tube? We're going to march! We'll bring our union banners, church banners, we'll make placards. Horwich Band has already said they'll come and lead us off from Euston Station. We'll make a grand show, believe me!"

Tickets for the train sold out within a couple of weeks. The local schools agreed to close down for the day and encourage the children to go down with their mums, dads, aunties and uncles. They even set to making their own banners.

"My dad wants his job – Save Horwich Works" one said. "Don't put my mum on the dole" shouted another, from the 7-year old daughter of Vanessa, from typing.

The Works Committee told management what was happening. The boss, Mr Barlow, wasn't too pleased about a day of lost production but he and his management team could see the sense of it – they'd be affected like everyone else if the works closed down. One day wouldn't make much difference.

Most of the marchers decided to join the train at their nearest station, Blackrod.

"We'll assemble at 06.00 at the works gate," Tommy announced, "and march behind Horwich Band down to the station. Bring your banners and placards. And just one thing. No drinking on th'way down. We're going to go to Parliament sober, that understood?"

There were a few moans and groans from the shop stewards but they could see his point. "We'll mek up for it on th'road back," Jack Halliwell said to his Machine Shop mate and fellow boozer Joe Cornthwaite, with a wink.

12th September dawned without a cloud in the sky, unusual for Horwich. About 400 of us assembled by the works gate, with the band tuning up and the banner of the Joint Shop Stewards Committee unfurled. There were other banners too, from the NUR, AEU, electricians, Boilermakers' Society, TSSA, Transport and General. Midge and her mate Sandra Walker were holding up the TSSA banner, amidst all the blokes. But there were church banners too, and lots of makeshift designs saying 'Save Our Works' and the like.

We set off in good spirits, assisted by our local bobby Joe Jolley, and marched down to the station. The band started off with 'Hail Smiling Morn' and progressed to 'Colonel Bogey', 'When the Saints Go Marching In' and 'Men of Harlech'.

We felt proud – of our work, and of our community. Of our class. My mum always used to say that hearing a brass band made her cry – and I could understand why as we walked down Station Road to catch our train.

It took us longer than we'd thought and the train was just coming into view as the first of us arrived on the platform.

It was hauled by a class 47 diesel loco complete with a specially-made headboard – 'SAVE HORWICH LOCO WORKS'. Some of the apprentice joiners had made it during their lunch breaks.

As the train approached, the driver gave a special rendition of 'Ilkley Moor Baht 'At'. Leaning out of the cab was former Bolton driver, Bert Westby, who'd transferred to Preston when the shed closed a few years back. He was in his element. The secondman was another ex-Bolton lad, Jim Whitehead.

"Are you comin' all th' way with us Bert?" Tommy shouted up.

"Wish we were owd lad but they'll put a leccy on at Stockport. A bit faster than us."

Everyone slowly piled on and the guard blew his whistle, getting a bit impatient and worrying about losing time. There were half as many people waving us off as were getting on the train, some with makeshift signs and banners saying 'Good Luck Horwich!'

Bert gave another noisy rendition as we set off and some of the apprentices had put down a few detonators on the track to give an added bit of fireworks. Fortunately they'd told the driver what to expect so he ignored the succession of bangs as the wheels of the loco passed over them.

The only other stop was at Bolton. We pulled in to find another big crowd waiting, with the Trades Council banner prominently displayed and many more, including the textile workers, printers, bleachers and dyers and engineers.

Midge and I had a compartment with Terry Dukinfield from The Paint Shop and his wife Marjorie who ran a fancy goods place on Lee Lane. We also had the company of Ezra Liptrot, long since retired from the Erecting Shop and bent double with arthritis. There was another woman, in her late 50s I'd say but quite smart looking, despite wearing jeans and jacket adorned with a 'Save Horwich Works' badge.

Midge was the first to recognise her. "Isn't it Mrs Barlow?" Midge enquired. She was the husband of George Barlow, the Works Manager. George had served his time at Horwich after the war and moved around to various railway workshops, first as a fitter and then going into management – at Derby, Crewe and Darlington. When Darlington was down to close he applied, and got, the top job at Horwich and had run the place since 1971.

"Yes that's right – I think I've seen you in the office when I've been in to see George. How do you do? My name's Enid by the way."

"And I'm Midge, and this is David who works in the Smithy, Terry and Marjorie, and Ezra."

"Oh yes I know Mr Liptrot, I was with my husband George when we presented you with a 40 year medal, do you remember?"

"Ah do that, and th'clock he gan me still keeps perfect time!"

Mrs Barlow, or for that matter her husband, didn't have a high profile in the town, though she was a member of the Methodist church choral society. Their performances of 'Messiah' each Christmas packed the church hall. Her husband played violin in the Horwich Orchestral Society.

"So you're on your own then today," Midge asked slightly coyly.

"Oh yes, George has to stay in the office, it wouldn't do for him to be seen on a demonstration, it's not really him. But I wanted to come and show my support, and I'm really here on behalf of us both."

"Well, if the Works closes it'll affect you as much as us," Midge offered.

"Well not really. George is coming up for retirement and he'll get a good railway pension. No, it's not about us, it's about this community. That's why I'm here, not out of self-interest. But – oh, I'm sorry I'm not suggesting you're here just for yourselves."

Horwich apprentices facing a bleak future. March 1983.

81

General view of the Erecting Shop at Horwich, with 313 015 receiving attention in March 1983.

"We don't want to lose our jobs, but it's about more than that, like you say".

We wound our way through the Manchester suburbs and reached Stockport, where our diesel was uncoupled and ran back past the train with Bert and Dave hanging out of the cab waving their caps and sounding their horn as they went.

"Daft buggers," said Midge, trying not to laugh.

The electric loco dropped down from the sidings and coupled on to our train and we were away, next stop London.

Terry and Marjorie were good company, Ezra didn't say much though and Mrs Barlow – who insisted on being called Enid – slowly came out of her reserve.

"I've brought some sandwiches and little cakes that I baked last night, would anyone care to try one?"

Ezra leapt forward and grabbed a big slice of Victoria Sponge. "Ah forgeet fert get mi breakfast this morn....this'll do t'job." We dipped into the dainty display of sandwiches, with me opting for the cheese and chutney while Midge tried one of the ham and mustard.

Midge and Enid got on well with each other, chatting about their choral singing, how they'd manage without the Works, and about their shared love of rambling.

"We've always been keen walkers," said Enid. "I was brought up in Derby, where I met George. My playground was the Peak District and we used to go out on the train most Sundays. Happy days. But I love the hills around Horwich – Rivington, Anglezarke, Great Hill. They aren't as dramatic as the Peak District but they have a peacefulness and solitude to them."

"Yes, I used to go out with my late husband most weekends up those hills, when we weren't off out on the bikes."

"Ah, Mr Wrightson. That was a terrible tragedy, you must have been heartbroken," Enid said.
"George was deeply upset. He has a tendency to blame himself for everything and he has never forgiven himself for not having that crane checked."

"It wasn't anyone's fault," said Midge. "He mustn't feel like that. And it was years ago, I've moved on – and remarried. Dave's my husband, as of three months ago! But you never quite get over it, even if he was a bit of a bugger at times."

We passed Stoke-on-Trent, Lichfield, Rugby, Bletchley. The landscape became richer, the houses bigger and neatly laid-out. We'd be in London in 20 minutes.

We arrived at Euston a couple of minutes early. In good traditional style we'd had a whip-round for the driver, secondman and guard – Manchester men, from Longsight and Piccadilly – who gave us all a friendly wave as we trooped up the ramp with our banners and placards.

Tommy Hindley was in charge of the arrangements and had planned the route with the police well before. Some of the coppers were a different kettle of fish from our local bobbies like Jimmy, whose wife was on the march with us. They looked miserable bastards, spoiling for a fight. They weren't going to get one though, not today.

We were joined at Euston by some of the more militant NUR members from London District Council. There was a token presence from the national executive, led by the deputy general secretary Derek Shaw, whom no-one outside the NUR had heard of. Pete Jagger, one of my Communist Party friends and a member of the district council, had just come off his early shift – he was a guard at Euston depot – and was going to join us. He was still in uniform, complete with his guard's leather bag.

Horwich Band assembled outside the station and struck up 'Knight Templar', a well-known march and highly appropriate, composed by a shopman from Shildon Works in Co. Durham. They were down to close as well.

We set off across Euston Road to toots from the taxi drivers and angry glares from the some of the car drivers forced to wait a few minutes while we got across.

"You bastards are running this country!" one of them yelled out of the safety of his car window.

Some of the women blew him a kiss.

"Remember now, don't respond to any provocation," Tommy reminded us from his megaphone. Most of the people who watched us as we marched down Tottenham Court Road were either nonplussed or supportive. Some of the shopworkers came out and applauded. Office workers, even a few city gents who still sported their traditional bowler hats, gave us friendly waves.

When the coppers realised we weren't intent on violent revolution, for the time being, they relaxed a bit and some shared fags with the stewards. Enid had got into her stride by now and was leading the chanting.

"What do we want?"

"Keep Our Jobs!"

"When do we want 'em?"

"Now!!"

Lacking in originality I know but it sent out the message to anyone who cared to listen. I tried to make up a good chant that rhymed with 'Horwich' but the best I could do was something about porridge.

A few hangers-on from the SWP were selling their papers and shouting 'General Strike – Now!' but they didn't raise much of a noise, or support. It took us nearly an hour to get near to

Parliament, we could see 'Big Ben' peeping out beyond the government buildings on Whitehall.

It was time to strike up the band again. The lads – and a few lasses – were in good form, playing 'Rimington' as we passed the gates to Downing Street. "Come on, play 'The Red Flag'" we all implored. They obliged – it's not a brilliant anthem but does go well when played by a brass band. My mum would have been in tears by now.

We stopped in Parliament Square and our local MPs were there to meet us – Albert Smith, the ageing Labour member for Horwich South and his younger pal Gary Stewart, for Bolton North. They were joined by Tom Simmons, the Tory for the newly-created seat of Westhoughton Central, which we thought was a railway station. About 50 of us had got clearance to go into the House of Commons itself, though most were happy enough to sit on the grass, eat our sandwiches and get slowly pissed.

Albert Smith was introduced by Tommy Hindley. In Labour Party terms, they were at opposite ends of the political spectrum, with Albert firmly on the right. There was no love lost between either of them but the day demanded unity and toleration.

"Brothers and sisters, I'm delighted that our local MP Albert Smith has put aside vital parliamentary business and come to address us. Mr Smith..."

"Well thank you Tom, thank you. Yes, well I've been your Member of Parliament, for Horwich South, over 40 years now and we've seen a few changes. As you know, I started my working life in the Loco Works and served my time in the Machine Shop before going to fight for King and Country. When I was elected in 1945 we had high hopes for our railways as part of the new Britain, and one of the first things the new Labour Government did was to nationalise them. We had ten years of growth and modernisation, but the tide was turning against the railways as people bought their cars. You can't halt progress. But we need to carry on building trains and, for me, they should be built at Horwich. Let 'em close down Doncaster, there are jobs in the coal mines..."

At this point some of the crowd was starting to get restless.

Johnny Gregson, one of the more volatile shop stewards, shouted out "No workshops should close! We're not here to put other people out of work!" A lot of voices piped up in support of Johnny.

"Come on lads, let Mr Smith finish," pleaded Tommy.

"Well yes, as I was saying. Let's face facts. We can't halt progress. I'm with you in your campaign but you know what the best way of succeeding is? I'll tell you. Elect a Labour Government. Thank you chairman."

Next to speak was Gary Stewart. He'd been MP for a few years after being parachuted in by the Labour Executive as a 'rising star'. He'd been a lawyer in Birmingham before then and spoke with a mild Brummy accent. He hadn't shown much interest in the campaign so far but he knew his seat was marginal and didn't want to lose his job in the next General Election.

"I'm delighted to welcome this amazing crowd to Parliament. I was moved to tears as I saw your banners coming down Whitehall...."

"Spare me, for Christ's sake", whispered Midge, who'd never liked him. Another careerist, she judged.

"The fight to save Horwich Works has got to be won. Like my colleague Albert says, the surest way to succeed is to elect a Labour Government and give Thatcher her marching orders."

"It were Labour that finished off Beeching's dirty work!" shouted Ernie Eccleston from the middle of the crowd. "Tha meyt be too young to remember it, but ah con!"

Stewart mumbled a few more platitudes about taking the case up with the Prime Minister and stood down. Applause was polite, but muted.

"Thank you Gary, we appreciate your support. Our final speaker is Tom Simmons, the Conservative MP for Westhoughton Central. Please give Mr Simmons a respectful hearing."

Simmons was greeted by a few groans and hisses from some of the younger end but people nudged them to be quiet and give the lad a hearing.

And he was a lad really, probably in his late 20s. He came from one of the old Lancashire families and owned half of the Pendle Forest. He looked nervous and you could hardly blame him.

"Thank you very much Mr Chairman, and thank you for coming down to London to make your voices heard. I suppose most of you didn't vote for me (cries of "Too bloody right!") and that's your privilege. But I was elected to serve all the people of my constituency, which almost touches on the Works site. Many of you live in Westhoughton and I understand how serious this threat is, to both Horwich and its neighbouring town. My only connection with the railways was my father, who was a director of the LMS. Yes, I'm from a privileged background but that doesn't mean to say I'm not going to stand up for what I believe is right. And you are right to fight this closure and I'll do everything in my power to help you win. I've an appointment tomorrow morning with the Transport Minister and I'm going to urge he changes his mind and instructs – and I mean 'instructs' – the British Railways Board to halt this closure. I don't believe in keeping factories going that have no future, but I'm convinced there is a future for Horwich Loco Works, doing what it does well – building trains. And if there is anything more I can do to help you, please just ask."

He got a round of respectful applause. Of all three he sounded the most sincere. And he was right, there were no votes for him in this.

Midge had got a pass to go into Parliament to see her MP, the less than charismatic Mr Smith. I'd been delegated to stay outside and steward the crowd. Which meant no drink, at least for the first half hour, or so. Pete had managed to get a pass so he could lobby his own MP, from one of the inner London suburbs, on the need for rail investment. I watched him trotting off by the St Stephen's entrance, looking forward to a cheap pint in the Stranger's Bar.

About 10 minutes later we heard a siren going off and lots of police suddenly appeared, with very real-looking machine guns.

"What the fuck's goin' on?" one of my mates asked.

"Wish I knew but it sounds like some sort of security alert. Hope it's nowt to do with us."

About half an hour later Pete emerged from the gates, assisted by two very large coppers. He looked unusually sheepish.

"What's happened?" I asked him.

"Well comrade it's all a bit embarrassing. I'd forgotten I had the can of dets in my guard's bag and it triggered off an alarm. When the cops opened the bag they found what to them

BREL (British Rail Engineering Ltd) organized a popular Open Day at Horwich on 30 August 1975.

looked like dangerous explosives. It took me a lot of effort to persuade them that they were railway detonators that you put on the track if your train had broken down. Fortunately one of the coppers was ex-railway and he recognised the dets. The copper said I was a stupid cunt and bloody lucky not to be arrested and sent down for carrying dangerous weapons into parliament. He said 'the last bloke to do that was Guy Fawkes and you know what happened to him'."

"Well for once I agree with the coppers," I told him. "Putting the uncalled-for sexist language aside, you are a fucking stupid bastard aren't you? And I suppose you'll be asking me for one of these bottles of ale now."

About an hour and three more bottles of Newcastle Brown later, Midge re-appeared.

"How did it go love?" I asked, nonchalantly, with Pete sat next to me all smiles.

"Oh it was alright. The interview was cut short because of some sort of security alert. Did you hear anything about it? There were armed police running round all over the place."

"No love, not a thing. Did you hear anything Pete?"

"No, nothing."

"What makes me think you're a couple of lying little buggers? But anyway, it felt like we were going through the motions. He said he'd come along to the next action committee meeting and ask questions in the house."

Our train was booked off Euston at 18.45, after the rush-hour had finished and giving us time to see some of the sights. A few of the lads said they were off to a strip club in Soho. Midge was caustic.

"About time you lot grew up, ogling some naked young woman. You should be ashamed of yourselves."

"It's only a bit of fun," said Jack Milligan, from the Foundry.

"Oh, right Jack, I'm sure your missus will agree when I mention it to her at the club on Saturday?"

"You wouldn't, would you?"

"You just wait and see. Anyroad, they cost an arm and leg to get in those places, you couldn't afford it."

The group of intending revellers slunk off, ending up in one of the pubs near Euston where they made a nuisance of themselves singing 'She's a Lassie from Lancashire' and 'Daisy' in a slightly aggressive display of local pride. Funny how the really corny old songs suddenly spring up when you've had a few, and you can remember every line.

It was a warm September day so we wandered down to the Thames Embankment with Enid and a few of the girls from the typing pool, including Vanessa.

"You know what we should do next time?" Vanessa asked of no-one in particular. "We should circle the House of Commons, with everyone holding hands saying 'Ommmmm.' And we should then get the place to levitate. It'd show them the spiritual power of the people."

"There's a few flaws in your strategy, Van," I suggested. "For one thing the Houses of Parliament face on to the River Thames on one side, so we'd get a bit wet trying to encircle the place. And what would you do after the place had been raised up a few feet? Let it fall down again?"

"Well OK, I know the idea seems slightly wacky and needs a bit more thought, but we do need to be more imaginative than just asking boring MPs for a few favours."

"Well that's for certain," said Midge. "I'm not sure what we've achieved from this junket but at least we've tried."

It was coming up to 6.00 so we headed for the tube and squeezed onto a train heading for Euston. We needed to be in good time to marshal the crowd and look out for any strays. The train would leave on the dot at 6.45, whether everyone was on or not.

The gate opened to let us onto the platform at 6.30 and Midge and her mate Erica from Accounts ticked everyone off as they went on. By 6.42 we were missing just three.

"It's those stupid buggers who were after going to that strip club!" Midge groaned. "Just wait til I get my hands on them."

At 6.43 there was a commotion on the concourse and the three lads – Jack Milligan, Joey Sumner and Graham Thwaite – pissed out of their heads singing 'Show me the way to go home' – ran down the ramp.

"Oh Midge, Mrs Wrightson, don't be cross with us, we got on the wrong train and ended up in bloody Walthamstow or somewhere....And I'm dying for a piss..."

"Well you're not pissing here, get on that bloody train, it's about to go...with or without you."

We dragged them on board and the guard raised his green flag, whistled, and we felt the tug of the loco as we set off for home.

We were all knackered, apart from Enid who seemed to have boundless energy.

"Well what are we going to do next?" she asked. "We've got to plan a campaign that'll make them sit up! Remember the Suffragettes!"

"Yes Enid," Midge replied. "But we don't want to be chaining ourselves to railings or throwing ourselves under horses, or trains. But I'm buggered if I do know what we should do."

"I know what!" said Enid. "Remember a few years ago the workers up in Glasgow who faced the same issue with the closure of their shipyard? They took over the shipyard and started a work-in. Why don't we do that at Horwich?"

"You mean Upper Clyde Shipbuilders?" I asked.

"Yes, that's it. Wasn't one of the leaders a communist, like you?" she asked pointedly.

"Errr yes, Jimmy Reid. A great guy. So you're saying we should take over the works and run it ourselves?"

"Yes, that's exactly what I'm saying!"

"Wow, that's really far out," said Vanessa, who'd joined us in our compartment.

"Well I think it's a good idea," said Midge. "It needs a lot of thought and careful planning. And they haven't actually said The Works is going to close on any particular date. It's out for 'consultation', which we know is just part of the game that we can't win."

"Right then Midge," I said as we whizzed through Wolverton, whose railway works was a shadow of its former self, employing a few hundred when thousands once worked there. "Are you going to raise this as a firm proposal at tomorrow's meeting of the action committee?"

"Too right I am!"

"That's so...far out," said Vanessa as she fell quietly to sleep and didn't wake up until we pulled in to Bolton.

The occupation started two months later.......

Rare night at the Railway Club

Dancing to the music: a local couple having a grand evening.

My name is Pat Laverty and I'm a Connemara man. I've been here some 50 years now, a platelayer at Bolton, part of the Byng Street Permanent Way gang.

Let me tell you about a rare old time we had, back in November 1982 I think it was. Not good at dates. Anyway, it was a dirty wet night and I'd been on 'fog duty', signed on at 6 a.m. and finished at 6 p.m. I'd just time to get home, have my tea and smarten up a bit.

We were all gathered in the Railway Club, off Manchester Road. It's not the same these days, not many railwaymen left. But back then you'd still get the drivers, guards and signalmen having a Friday night drink. A few of us P-Way men as well.

It wasn't a palace but they did a grand pint of Guinness. That night it was full. Word had got round that Josef Locke, the great Irish tenor, was appearing. What little advertising there was referred to 'Mr X'. He was on the run – non-payment of income tax and various court summonses. Whether calling himself Mr X fooled the tax men and police I doubt.

The good and the bad of Bolton's Irish community were crowded into the club as well as the usual railway crowd. Building workers, local councillors, labourers, loafers. Not an unintelligent bunch by any means, and some fine singers amongst them as well as heavy drinkers.

I got there for 8.00 and shared a table with a few friends from the union and Labour Party. Noel, Guy, Peter and Maggie. They'd already had a few and were on good form with stories of some of the old characters who used to frequent the less salubrious pubs of Bolton, like The Kickin' Donkey and The Skennin' Door.

We expected Joe Locke to be on at about 9.00. He was notoriously unpunctual; the advert had said 8.00. At about 9.15 the bar telephone rang. Gerry, the club steward, answered the phone. We could hear "yes Joe," "certainly Joe", "Not a problem at all Joe."

"Right, just quieten down a bit please," appealed Gerry. "That was Mr X on the phone. His flight from Dublin has been delayed due to fog over the Irish Sea but he landed safely at Manchester 10 minutes ago. He's on his way."

We returned to the serious business of drinking Guinness and debating the terrible state of the world. Declan Carroll got out his accordion and some of the more outgoing sorts had a dance or two.

Half an hour passed and Mick suggested that we should have a few songs. "Any volunteers?"

Nobody made any move to stand up. Noel gave Pat Nolan a dig in the ribs. "Get up there and do a few of the old songs, there's a good man."

Pat stood up. He was from Claremorris, a Mayo man. A big fella, came to Bolton to work on the building sites and met a mill girl called Teresa – lovely and from Limerick – and settled down.

There was still plenty of talk going on. Gerry hammered on the bar with the stick he normally used when things got out of hand.

"Be quiet for the love of God will ye? Pat's going to give us a couple of songs while we wait for Joe – sorry, Mr X."

"Thank you Gerry. Here's one we used to sing after a hard day on the sites, by a Dublin man by the name of Dominic Behan, with whom I had the privilege of working when I was a lad down in London."

As down the glen, came McAlpine's men
With their shovels slung behind them.
Twas in the pub that they drank their sub
And up in the Spike you'll find 'em.
McAlpine's God was a well-filled hod
With your shoulders cut to bits and seared.
If you pride your life, don't join by Christ,
with McAlpine's Fusiliers...

The room exploded with applause. Half of the lads in the room had worked on the sites and knew what the life was like. Bloody awful. Pat entertained us with a few more. Roddy McCorley, Carrickfergus, Forty Shades of Green. Some of the more sentimental amongst us shed a tear at the memories of the old country and a world we'd lost.

A classic Bolton Irish pub scene with a thoughtful-looking drinker enjoying his pipe and a pint of Guinness c 1980.

The room settled back into comfortable chaos. No sign of Mr X.

Each time the door opened the place went quiet; but it wasn't him. Another call suggested he'd got stuck in a road accident in Salford, but was on his way.

We had more songs, with accordion accompaniment. Maggie Gallagher did a lovely rendition of 'She Moves Through the Fair'. You could've heard a pin drop.....

Last night she came to me
My true love came in
And softly she came
That her feet made no din
And she laid her hand on me
And this she did say
It will not be long, love
Till our wedding day.....

We had plenty more songs. It became more raucous and Republican. We all stood up to sing 'The Men Behind The Wire', led by Noel. Jimmy McManus's brother was one of them, banged up in Long Kesh.

By 2.00 there was still no sign of Mr X. The phone had stopped ringing. Maybe the police had caught up with him. By then, we didn't care.

At 3.00 Gerry got out his stick and hammered on the bar. "Will all of yous go home now!"

"Why's that Gerry, for the love of God? We're having a great time," shouted Mick Molloy, a bit the worse for wear.

"Because you've drunk us out of beer, whisky and everytin' else, that's why."

"Well we won't be going anywhere until we've sung the National Anthem," Kevin McLoughlin announced.

A few of our English friends were a bit surprised that we should want to do that, after all that had been said and sung. We got to our feet. It was our own national anthem:

"Soldiers are we
whose lives are pledged to Ireland
Some have come
from a land beyond the wave
Sworn to be free
No more our ancient sire land
Shall shelter the despot or the slave
Tonight we man the gap of danger
In Erin's cause, come woe or weal
'Mid cannons' roar and rifles peal
We'll chant a soldier's song.."

We shuffled out of the club, dissolving into the Bolton drizzle. It was nearly 4 a.m. by now.

I was half-way along Crescent Road, just by Beehive Mill, when a car stopped by me. The window came down and a smart-looking chap with a wee moustache leaned out. I recognised the face from the newspapers.

"Excuse me...would you happen to know where The Railwaymen's Social Club is?"

Irish music was widespread in most Lancashire towns in the 1970s and 1980s. This accordion player was a popular local musician in the Bolton area.

Popular local Irish band 'The Fontaines' performing in Bolton, c 1980.

Last Train from Blackstock Junction

I hate Beeching. Smarmy upper class shit from East Grinstead. I was only 12 at the time he closed our station down. But we didn't let it go quietly.

Sorry about the language. Some readers may be offended. Don't mean to. But fuck Beeching, fuck Marples and fuck all the toadies who went along with it, closing down the railways, including Harold Wilson and his ridiculous mac and pipe, which he never really puffed on anyway.

The worst of all are the clever-arses who say that Beeching was 'just a product of his time' and that 'everyone knew the railways were a thing of the past'. Well I didn't and I was just a working class kid from Blackstock. I could see that more and more cars would ruin our towns and screw the environment. And I wasn't the only one.....

People know me as a gentle bloke. But sometimes you need to be angry. Being nice has never changed much. Tell the Ukrainians to be 'nice' when they've got a bloody big Russian tank coming down their street. Offer the Ruskis some sweeties, see what that gets you.

Rant over, get on with the story Peter (that's me, or just 'Pete' Jackson).

Sign of the times: Closure notice at Tyledsley station on the Manchester–Leigh–Wigan Line. The line closed and part of the route is now a busway.

I was brought up in Blackstock, a small mill town near Bolton. Our main station was Blackstock Junction, from where the 'little puffer', as we used to call it as children, used to run up to Blackstock Town station. It stopped puffing in 1961. Within a few years the branch platforms were overgrown with weeds and the station signs had been pinched by souvenir hunters.

The town was dominated by one spinning mill, Nuttall's – but it was massive. When I was a kid it still employed about 400, mostly women who lived in the village. My mum included. I used to take her a flask and sandwich when she was on the evening 'housewives' shift'.

Like other Blackstock 'housewives', she had a life of leisure the rest of the day. Apart from bringing us up, doing the shopping, cooking, washing and cleaning. Dad was a fitter in Bolton, at Hick Hargreaves, so he could jump on a train and be at his tools within 10 minutes. Until that fucking Beeching came along. OK, I'll stop it.

I'd just passed my 11 plus and had started at Thornleigh, the local Catholic grammar run by a bunch of mildly eccentric priests. Correction, some of them were completely nuts. I'd really wanted to go somewhere that required a train journey but my bike had to do. I really envied the lads from Wigan and Bury who came in every day on a steam train. Lucky sods. They used to rub it in by telling me which rare locos they'd seen that morning.

I was a train spotter, you've probably guessed by now. A figure of fun for idiot petrol-heads but I wear my spotters' badges with pride, or at any rate I used to. Going round collecting engine

Lostock Junction, c November 1966. Note the well-tended garden and Heaton's Mill in the background. The Lostock Arms remains but is currently empty. The station closed but re-opened in 1989, but only serving the Preston Line (in the foreground). There are aspirations to re-instate the Wigan platforms.

numbers gave me a brilliant knowledge of British geography, at least where the railways went (until, obviously...but I'll not go there). It taught me to read maps and timetables. Locomotive names gave me a knowledge of people, at least the upper class, places, army regiments, and the great houses of England. 'Our' Empire. All useful stuff for an aspiring revolutionary. But I wasn't that kind of revolutionary. If I had heroes, they were Gandhi and Martin Luther King. But we all know what happened to them. They were too nice, too.

The Beeching Report was published in 1963 and there in the small print, among stations to close, was 'Blackstock Junction'. It was listed alphabetically, sandwiched between Black Bank and Bolham Water, wherever they were. But we weren't some tiny village in the middle of nowhere. Blackstock, even then, was bigger than most towns in Devon or Norfolk. There was a bus to Bolton every hour and it took ages. We were told that was 'sufficient' – sufficient for us northern peasants, that is.

Everyone was pissed off. But nobody did anything. "Oh, you can't stand in the way of progress," some morons trotted out. It wasn't 'progress' for us.

Mr Khan, the station master, was in tears when the news appeared in the local paper. It was a Saturday morning and I'd cycled down to the station for a chat. We all loved Mr Khan. A rarity back then, an Asian guy running a station. He'd transformed the gardens since he took over three years ago, planted some vegetables as well as roses and hydrangeas. Even some of our local racists admitted he was a decent sort, "not like the rest of 'em", as if they had any idea what 'the rest of them' were like.

"Blackstock Junction station to close" was the headline in The Bolton Evening News. They even published the date of closure – 6th November 1966. It seemed that people had already been given the chance to object but we didn't know anything about it. They'd kept that quiet.

"It was my dream to have my own station," he told me, "ever since I started on the railway as a porter. I've got more people using the trains, I've created this nice little garden. All for nothing."

He opened the door and let me into the booking office; I made him a cup of his favourite Darjeeling tea in between serving the customers. I'd developed a good knowledge of the ticketing system and Mr Khan was happy to let me 'get on with it' while he read the paper. Everyone was saying how terrible it was, but no-one was willing to go to the barricades.

That evening a few of us met for our weekly session on the footbridge, seeing what was on 'the Glasgow' and some of the other remaining steam-hauled trains in between the despised diesels.

"If nobody else is going to protest, at least we should," I announced. "Who's for joining the campaign?"

The other lads shuffled around a bit and I put on my impatient expression. It was agreed that "something should be done."

We set up 'The Action Committee', a secret society dedicated to saving our station and Mr Khan's job.

We decided to produce a leaflet and put it through every letterbox in the village. We'd write to our MP.

We had just six weeks before the station was to close. Looking back we hadn't a cat in hell's chance but, come on, we were 12 year old kids. All this stuff was new to us and we had the giddy optimism of boyhood – not even youth.

I did most of the writing, with a bit of help from Geoff and Colin. We saw it as a rallying cry. The leaflet was dated 29th October 1966 and read:

"People of Blackstock! On the above date Blackstock Junction station will be closed to all traffic. It is only one of hundreds of small stations which are being done away with. They've already closed Blackstock Town station. Before long, lines such as Bolton to Bury and Blackstock to Wigan could be at risk if you do not use the trains. Don't let other stations such as Blackrod or Bradley Fold go the same way as Blackstock Junction. Closing our station will mean more cars on the already congested roads. It will mean children can't get to school unless a bus is provided. In years to come, we will look back on this madness and wish we had kept our railways. Write to your MP and don't let them do it. The railways need your custom. Why don't YOU travel by train?"

We weren't sure how to sign it. 'The Action Committee'? A protest campaign? We settled on 'The youth of Blackstock', since our committee was supposed to be top secret. It was maybe a bit presumptuous as most of the youth of Blackstock didn't seem to give a shit.

I got one of the friendlier priests at school to type it out on the school's office typewriter. We needed to run a few hundred copies off at least. We bribed the school secretary to use the high-tech Gestetner copier that she treated as her prize personal possession. A nice box of Thornton's chocolates did the job.

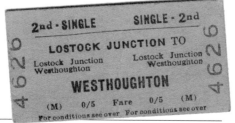

Mr Atcha, 'station-master, Lostock Junction' pictured at his station on 4th November 1966, a couple of days before closure (the last train ran on 5th November as there was no Sunday service). He had gone to the trouble of removing the posters from the noticeboards.

The leaflet was only a qualified success, it has to be admitted. We'd neglected to put a contact address 'for more information' and none of us had a phone at home. Maybe the outraged citizenry of Blackstock was quietly lobbying their MP, or even preparing for armed insurrection. If you were, obviously, you'd keep mum about it.

We received a perfunctory letter from our MP. He thanked us for going to the trouble of writing about the closure of 'Blackpool Junction' and informed us that every effort was being made to provide alternative transport for "those few users who may suffer hardship."

By now we were into October, not much time left. We realised the last train was scheduled to run on the Saturday evening – 5th November. There hadn't been a Sunday service for years. We held a further meeting of the Action Committee and resolved that if our just demands (viz. to remind you, retention of the station and keeping Mr Khan as station master) were not met, we would resort to direct action.

This would comprise setting off a blitzkrieg of fireworks and laying dozens of detonators on the track when the train departed from the station. Beeching would hear the explosions at home in bloody East Grinstead. At least Blackstock Junction would go out with a bang, and our point would have been made. Honour would be satisfied – we'd fought and lost, but....It was like Patrick Pearse's 'blood sacrifice' of Easter 1916, running fifty years' late.

We knew of an old platelayer's hut not far away, on the defunct branch line to Blackstock Town, that might have a few detonators stored away which nobody really wanted. These were the small parcels of explosive that railwaymen put on the track to stop a train in an emergency. We considered this was a real emergency, the closing down of our station, so all tactics were justified.

You can't make an omelette....

On Wednesday night we each donned our balaclavas – knitted by our mothers – and cycled up to the old sidings where the cabin was located. We jumped over the fence and scrambled down the embankment. The door to the cabin was unlocked, with an old rusty sign warning 'Danger – Explosives'.

We beheld a treasure trove of railway detonators. We came away with five bags of them, carrying about a dozen in each of our saddlebags. We were a bit worried that they might explode as we bounced along the cobbled streets, but we exercised caution and kept in a low gear. Mrs Timpson was just shutting up shop as we cycled, surreptitiously, past. "A bit early in the year for balaclavas isn't it Peter?" she said.

Our horde was secreted in various bike sheds and greenhouses, out of sight of inquisitive parents or potential informers. Those of us who could afford to bought extra supplies of fireworks from the local shop.

"You're going t'be havin' fun on Sat'day, aren't you?" Mrs Timpson asked Colin, who came away with a large bag of air bombs. "Plannin' fert start World War 3?"

We left feeling slightly worried. Did she know? Probably not, but we couldn't be sure. It seemed unlikely that Mrs Timpson was in the pay of the Railway Police, or MI5.

Our plans were taking shape quite well. Word had gone round that the last train was going to have a big send-off and other kids said they'd bring fireworks to set off when the train arrived. We kept quiet about the detonators. We didn't want anyone spilling the beans to the authorities.

A final part of the plan was to ensure that the driver and guard of the last train were aware that something was being planned for the Saturday night. As luck would have it the driver of the Friday night train – 9.45 from Blackstock, a Blackpool–Manchester stopper was also rostered for the Saturday.

On the Friday evening we had a quick word when the diesel train stopped and whispered conspiratorially that 'something was being planned' for tomorrow but he wasn't to worry. The Action Committee had everything in hand but he might hear a few bangs.

"Aw've heard nowt," was the knowing reply.

During Saturday we paid our last respects to the station and we all called in for a cup of tea with Mr Khan. His mood hadn't lifted. We found him stripping the outside notice boards of posters advertising day excursions to Blackpool and Southport.

"They are sending me to Manchester Victoria," he wailed. "It's a terrible place, full of foreigners."

He closed the booking office at 14.00h and we each purchased a souvenir ticket, the cheapest ones we could. I got a child single to Bolton, for 6d. I still treasure it.

As darkness fell our small team of saboteurs brought out the ammunition – six bags of detonators. We brought them down to the station in readiness for the train. Other members set up ranks of fireworks along the back of the platform, including the 20 or so air bombs from Colin's supply.

The plan was to wait until the signal for the train went off – operated by Blackstock Junction signalbox - and then five of us would jump down onto the track and place all the detonators just in advance of where the train would come to a stand. When it set off, there would be a cacophony of explosions that would be heard in Westhoughton, or maybe even Ince and East Grinstead!

At exactly 9.42 the signal went up. The last train was running on time; we had three minutes. We donned our balaclavas and jumped down from the platform, spreading the detonators along about 25 yards of track. Our co-conspirators in charge of the firework display got ready to light the charges.

The next two minutes were agonising. We heard a rumbling in the distance, the sound of a train, going rather fast. It was Colin, a bit of a diesel buff, who first said there was something not quite right. "That's not a diesel railcar engine, sounds more like a Class 47..."

Before we had time for further analysis, the shape of a class 47 express loco came into view, clearly with no intention of stopping at anywhere as humble as Blackstock Junction.

"Oh bloody hell," shouted Geoff. "It's the Glasgow running late..."

The train came rushing past us and set off a series of very loud explosions. The detonators were packed so closely together that it almost merged into a single prolonged 'boom'.

The driver of the express applied his emergency brake to the sound of screeches and a hail of sparks from the brake blocks. We looked on aghast as the train came to a very rapid stop just by the signalbox.

We could hear a lot of angry shouting going on in the distance, in the direction of the becalmed engine.

After a few minutes the train moved away. We found out later that the signalman had been tipped off that 'summat was up' but hadn't quite expected such a spectacular carry-on with his premier train of the day. He was very cross.

We could only stand and...wait. The signal came off again a few minutes later and the now-delayed stopper pulled in, for the very last time, to Blackstock Junction.

The driver leaned out of his cab. "No fireworks then?"

We mumbled that plans had changed and it was to be a more solemn farewell.

The mood was subdued, to say the least. Colin let off a couple of air bombs as a token gesture and the crowd of would-be revellers boarded the train. It moved off with a long sad note on the horn. At the back of the crowd I caught sight of Mr Khan, waving us, and his dreams, goodbye. Only Manchester Victoria beckoned, come Monday morning early turn.

As the train gathered speed and passed under Manchester Road bridge we heard police sirens in the distance. Probably just more Bonfire Night mayhem, though the headlights seemed to head for the station. But we were on our way, making good our escape.

On arrival at Bolton we decided discretion was the better part of valour and the Action Committee dispersed through the goods yard, rather than risk arrest at the ticket barriers. None of us were particularly keen on the prospect of a year in some awful Borstal.

Fifty years later, Blackstock Station – though no longer a junction – re-opened. It's now an unstaffed halt. Someone had a sense of historical irony: the re-opening day was November 5th 2016. Members of the Action Committee were not official invitees but we turned up all the same, minus balaclavas.

Our ranks included a retired police superintendent, railway operations manager, university professor and a company managing director.

We debated putting on a re-enactment of Bonfire Night, 1966, but thought the better of it. Someone might've got hurt, or arrested!